MATHS

for ages 10 - 11

Addition

Subtraction

Multiplication

Division

Decimals

Area

Perimeter

Symmetry and Shapes

Volume

Percentages

Fractions

Coordinates

Length

Capacity

Square Numbers

Handling Data

Probability

Addition Revision

Answer these addition questions as quickly as you can:

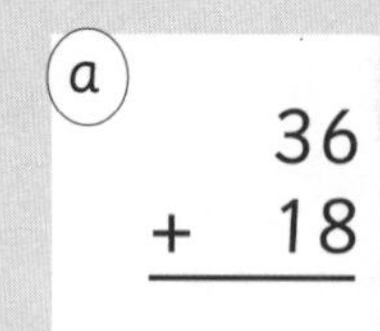

a	b	c	d	e
36 + 18	47 + 23	58 + 39	76 + 28	82 + 19

f	g	h	i	j
324 + 48	519 + 87	699 + 51	857 + 82	436 + 188 + 67

It is very important to work tidily...

Minnie

...and to make sure that you always keep the units in line.

Max

Now try these questions.
Work in an exercise book or on a separate piece of paper. Make sure that you work tidily and that you keep the units in line.

k) 94 + 13	l) 48 + 36	m) 85 + 85	n) 76 + 58
o) 218 + 31	p) 579 + 82	q) 783 + 65	r) 647 + 299 + 6
s) 392 + 417 + 16	t) 446 + 317 + 85 + 9	u) 858 + 614	

Max

The answer to question u was more than 1000.

Now answer the questions which include thousands at the top of page 3.

Minnie

(a) 2437 + 618

(b) 5614 + 2198

Remember, always keep the units in line.

Look at this question:

4682 + 3 + 28 + 396

	Th	H	T	U
	4	6	8	2
		3	9	6
			2	8
+				3
	5	1	0	9

Now try these:

(c) 32 + 2194 + 6 + 487

(d) 718 + 59 + 693 + 3288

In both of the questions below, we use the column next to the thousands column.
It is called the ten-thousands column.

(e)

	3	3	4	1	6
+		8	2	7	4

(f)

	5	2	3	2	9
+	1	7	2	5	2

In the next two we are going to use the hundred-thousand column as well.

(g)

	2	1	4	1	6	8
+		3	7	2	9	4

(h)

	6	2	4	7	9	8
+	2	3	6	5	0	2

Try this question which uses the millions column:

(i) 5842396 + 265717

Mental Speed

Time yourself to see how quickly you can answer these questions in your head.

1) 42 + 18
2) 38 + 12
3) 56 + 24
4) 85 + 15
5) 36 + 64
6) 72 + 18
7) 33 + 27
8) 21 + 19
9) 58 + 42
10) 67 + 23
11) 16 + 16
12) 19 + 19
13) 14 + 14
14) 12 + 12
15) 18 + 18
16) 13 + 13
17) 17 + 17
18) 15 + 15
19) 35 + 35
20) 45 + 45

Time taken:

☐ seconds.

Subtraction Revision

Answer these subtraction questions as quickly as you can.
ALWAYS START WITH THE UNITS.
If there are not enough units, make some from a ten.
If there are not enough tens, make some from a hundred.
Remember that if you already have enough,
you don't need to make extra units or tens.

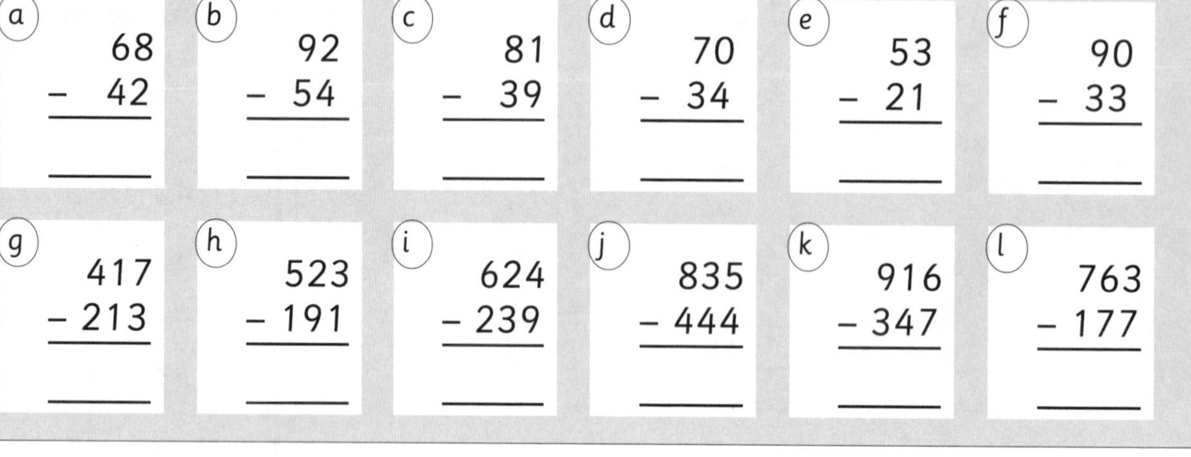

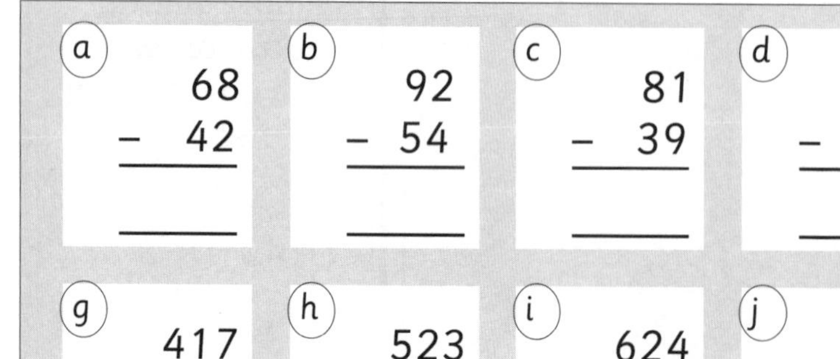

a	b	c	d	e	f
68 − 42	92 − 54	81 − 39	70 − 34	53 − 21	90 − 33

g	h	i	j	k	l
417 − 213	523 − 191	624 − 239	835 − 444	916 − 347	763 − 177

Sometimes we haven't got enough units on the top line but there aren't any tens to make more units from.

When this happens, we make ten tens using one of the hundreds, then we use one of the tens to make the units.

Minnie

Max

Look at this example:

7 0 3 − 2 4 8	First, ⇨ make some tens.	$^{6}\not{7}\,{}^{1}0\,3$ − 2 4 8	Now, ⇨ make some units and subtract	$^{6}\not{7}\,{}^{9}\not{1}\!\not{0}\,{}^{1}3$ − 2 4 8 = 4 5 5

Now try these:

m	n	o	p	q	r
501 − 189	807 − 599	600 − 82	900 − 123	704 − 352	405 − 127

Now try these questions, some of which include numbers in the thousands and ten-thousands columns:

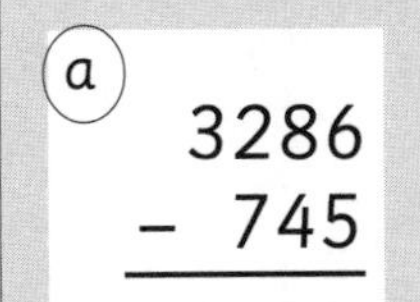

a) 3286 − 745 = ______

b) 5914 − 1273 = ______

c) 6218 − 4391 = ______

d) 7003 − 1517 = ______

e) 9085 − 3162 = ______

f) 12519 − 9182 = ______

g) 32647 − 17107 = ______

h) 79203 − 42139 = ______

i) 81000 − 55619 = ______

j) 100000 − 25000 = ______

We can use subtraction for finding change.

For example,
If I buy a book for £6·95, how much change will I have from a £20 note?

… Look:

£20·00
−£ 6·95
£13·05

k) £10·00 − £3·45 = ______

l) £20·00 − £1·96 = ______

m) £50·00 − £23·48 = ______

n) £80·00 − £24·95 = ______

o) £25·00 − £12·50 = ______

p) £100·00 − £54·72 = ______

Remember: Sometimes it is quicker and easier to work out some questions in your head.

Mental Speed

Time yourself to see how quickly you can answer these questions in your head.

1) 100 − 18 =
2) 100 − 25 =
3) 100 − 46 =
4) 100 − 54 =
5) 100 − 82 =
6) 100 − 91 =
7) 100 − 39 =
8) 100 − 77 =
9) 100 − 63 =
10) 100 − 75 =
11) 90 − 18 =
12) 80 − 25 =
13) 70 − 46 =
14) 80 − 54 =
15) 60 − 23 =
16) 40 − 17 =
17) 50 − 25 =
18) 500 − 25 =
19) 800 − 75 =
20) 600 − 50 =

Time taken: ______ seconds.

Using Decimals

Look carefully at these numbers:

Now look at these:

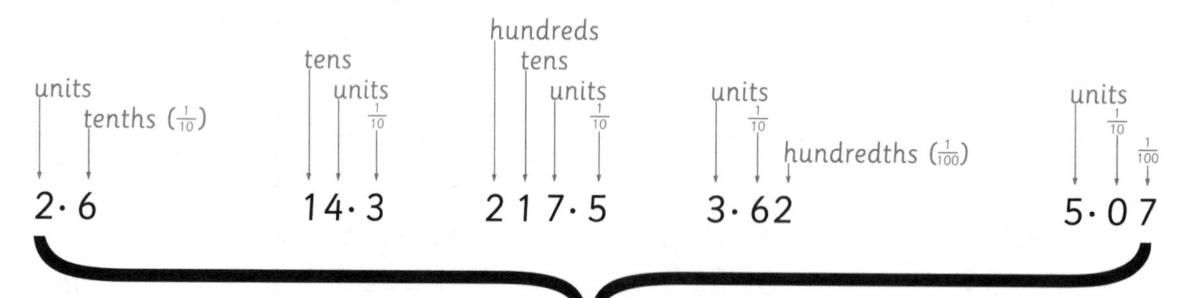

These are called decimal numbers.
In each one, next to the units is the decimal point,
next to the decimal point is the tenths column.

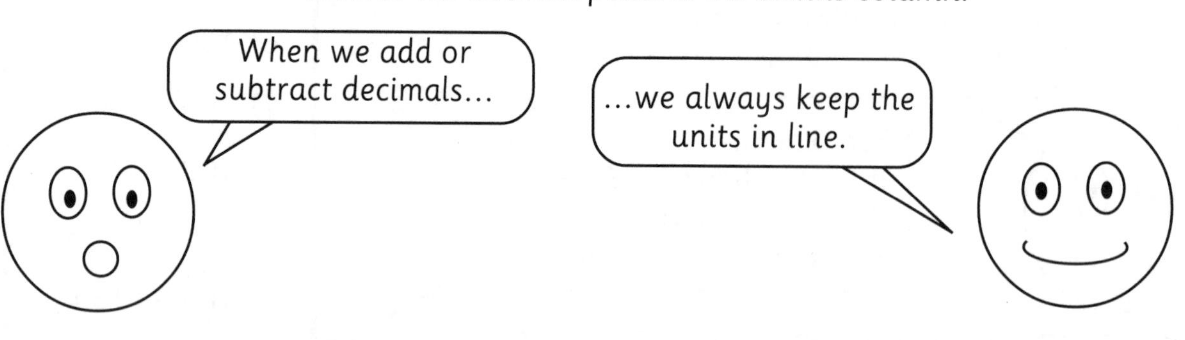

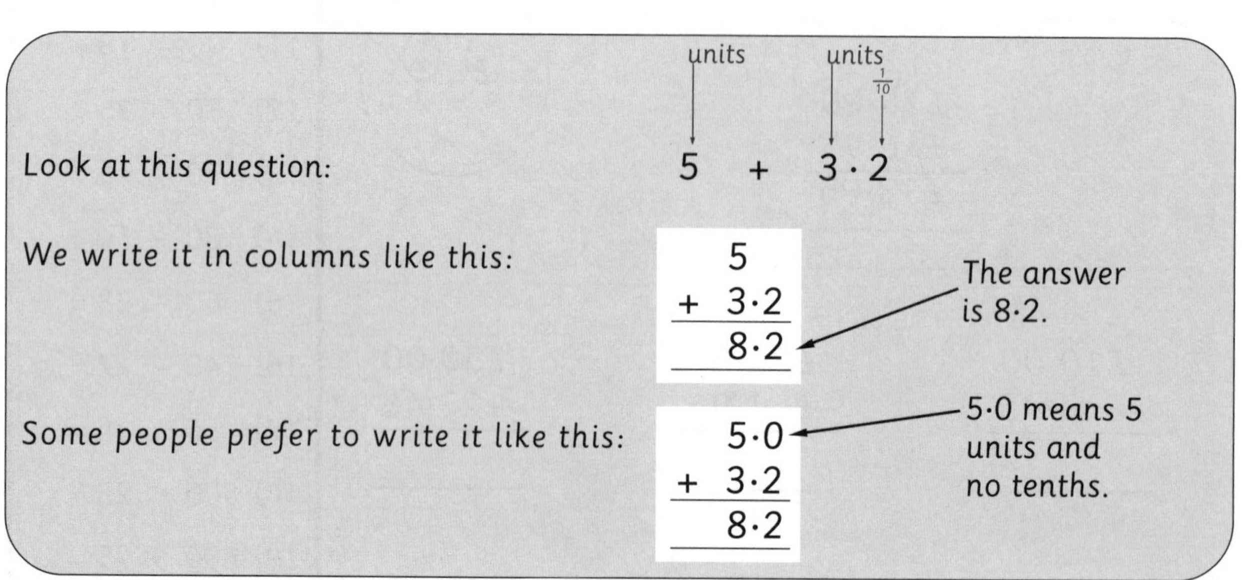

Try these questions:

(a) 3·4 + 2·3	(b) 7 + 1·9	(c) 6 + 3·4	(d) 5 + 1·7
(e) 6·3 + 2·1	(f) 12·2 + 5·9	(g) 23·4 + 6·7	

Here is another example:

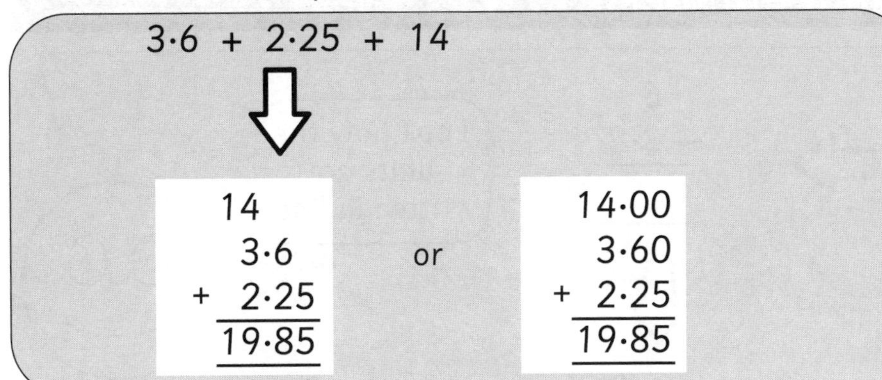

Notice that the units are all in line...

...and so are the decimal points.

Now try these questions:

(a) 7·2 + 6·45 + 12

(b) 13·6 + 9·83

(c) 25·25 + 1·75

(d) 16 + 7·8 + 11·39

(e) 126·4 + 19·37

(f) 68·39 + 31·61

(g)

Two teams competed in a 50m shuttle relay race.
These are the times in seconds which they recorded:

	First Runner	Second Runner	Third Runner	Fourth Runner
Red Team	9·32	8·79	10·22	8·60
Blue Team	9·83	8·81	9·04	8·58

i) What is the total time for the Red Team?

ii) What is the total time for the Blue Team?

iii) Which team won overall?

Mental Speed

Time yourself to see how quickly you can answer these questions in your head.

1) 6·2 + 3·1
2) 5·1 + 2·7
3) 2·6 + 1·2
4) 4·3 + 2·5
5) 7·6 + 3·3
6) 8·4 + 4·5
7) 9·1 + 6·8
8) 6·5 + 5·2
9) 8·8 + 3·1
10) 2·6 + 5·1
11) 3·6 + 2·7
12) 4·9 + 3·8
13) 5·7 + 1·9
14) 8·5 + 1·6
15) 3·5 + 2·5
16) 7·8 + 5·6
17) 9·5 + 3·5
18) 6·8 + 6·8
19) 0·25 + 0·75
20) 0·25 + 0·25

Time taken:

☐ seconds.

Subtracting decimal numbers

Look at this example:

$6 - 3{\cdot}8$ ⇨

$$\begin{array}{r} 6 \\ -\ 3{\cdot}8 \\ \hline \\ \hline \end{array}$$

⇩

$$\begin{array}{r} 6{\cdot}0 \\ -\ 3{\cdot}8 \\ \hline \\ \hline \end{array}$$

⇩

$$\begin{array}{r} {}^{5}\not{6}{\cdot}{}^{1}0 \\ -\ 3{\cdot}8 \\ \hline 2{\cdot}2 \\ \hline \end{array}$$

We have used one of the units to make ten tenths

...so $6 - 3{\cdot}8 = 2{\cdot}2$

Look how the units are written in line.

The subtraction is easier to do if you put a zero in the tenths column.

Here are two more examples:

$4{\cdot}8 - 3{\cdot}2$ ⇨

$$\begin{array}{r} 4{\cdot}8 \\ -\ 3{\cdot}2 \\ \hline 1{\cdot}6 \\ \hline \end{array}$$

$7{\cdot}3 - 2{\cdot}9$ ⇨

$$\begin{array}{r} {}^{6}\not{7}{\cdot}{}^{1}3 \\ -\ 2{\cdot}9 \\ \hline 4{\cdot}4 \\ \hline \end{array}$$

Try these subtractions:

(a) $6{\cdot}4 - 2{\cdot}1$	(b) $9{\cdot}7 - 3{\cdot}5$	(c) $8{\cdot}1 - 3{\cdot}8$	(d) $7 - 1{\cdot}9$
(e) $11{\cdot}3 - 4{\cdot}6$	(f) $18 - 7{\cdot}9$	(g) $33{\cdot}4 - 21{\cdot}7$	(h) $58{\cdot}9 - 31{\cdot}2$
(i) $72{\cdot}6 - 14{\cdot}8$	(j) $125{\cdot}6 - 58{\cdot}7$	(k) $217{\cdot}8 - 84{\cdot}3$	
(l) $345 - 126{\cdot}4$	(m) $70 - 39{\cdot}8$	(n) $100 - 63{\cdot}7$	

Look carefully at these examples:

8·65 − 3·28 ⇨

$$\begin{array}{r} 8\cdot\overset{5}{\not6}{}^{1}5 \\ -\ 3\cdot28 \\ \hline 5\cdot37 \end{array}$$

7 − 1·95 ⇨

$$\begin{array}{r} {}^{6}\not7\cdot\overset{9}{\not0}{}^{1}0 \\ -\ 1\cdot95 \\ \hline 5\cdot05 \end{array}$$

200 − 65·48 ⇨

$$\begin{array}{r} \overset{1}{\not2}\,\overset{9}{\not0}\,\overset{9}{\not0}\cdot\overset{9}{\not0}\,{}^{1}0 \\ -\ 6\,5\cdot4\,8 \\ \hline 1\,3\,4\cdot5\,2 \end{array}$$

Now try these questions:

(a) 7·39 − 4·27

(b) 8·46 − 6·98

(c) 14 − 3·62

(d) 9 − 2·75

(e) 67 − 31·64

(f) 18·3 − 9·73

(g)

This is the chart of times in seconds recorded by the Red and Blue teams in the 50m shuttle relay.

	First Runner	Second Runner	Third Runner	Fourth Runner
Red Team	9·32	8·79	10·22	8·60
Blue Team	9·83	8·81	9·04	8·58

i) The fourth runner was the Red Team's fastest. Which runner was the Red Team's slowest?

ii) Which runner was the Blue Team's slowest?

iii) How much faster was the Blue Team's third runner than the Red Team's third runner?

Mental Speed

Time yourself to see how quickly you can answer these questions in your head.

1) 6·4 − 3·2
2) 5·4 − 2·4
3) 8·4 − 1·6
4) 9·4 − 6·5
5) 6·4 − 2·3
6) 7·4 − 1·4
7) 4·4 − 2·1
8) 5·4 − 4·3
9) 8·4 − 4·2
10) 1·4 − 0·5
11) 6·4 − 5·2
12) 6 − 4·2
13) 6 − 3·2
14) 6 − 2·2
15) 6 − 1·2
16) 6 − 0·2
17) 10 − 7·5
18) 10 − 2·5
19) 10 − 6·1
20) 10 − 8·7

Time taken:

☐ seconds.

Shapes on a grid

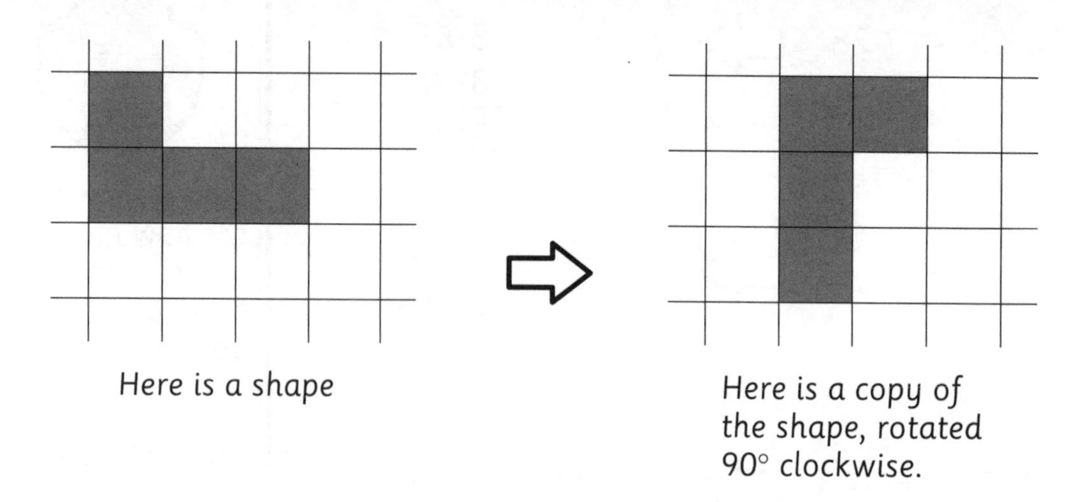

Use grid paper to draw the shapes below.
Follow the instructions carefully.
You can photocopy page 11 if you wish to.

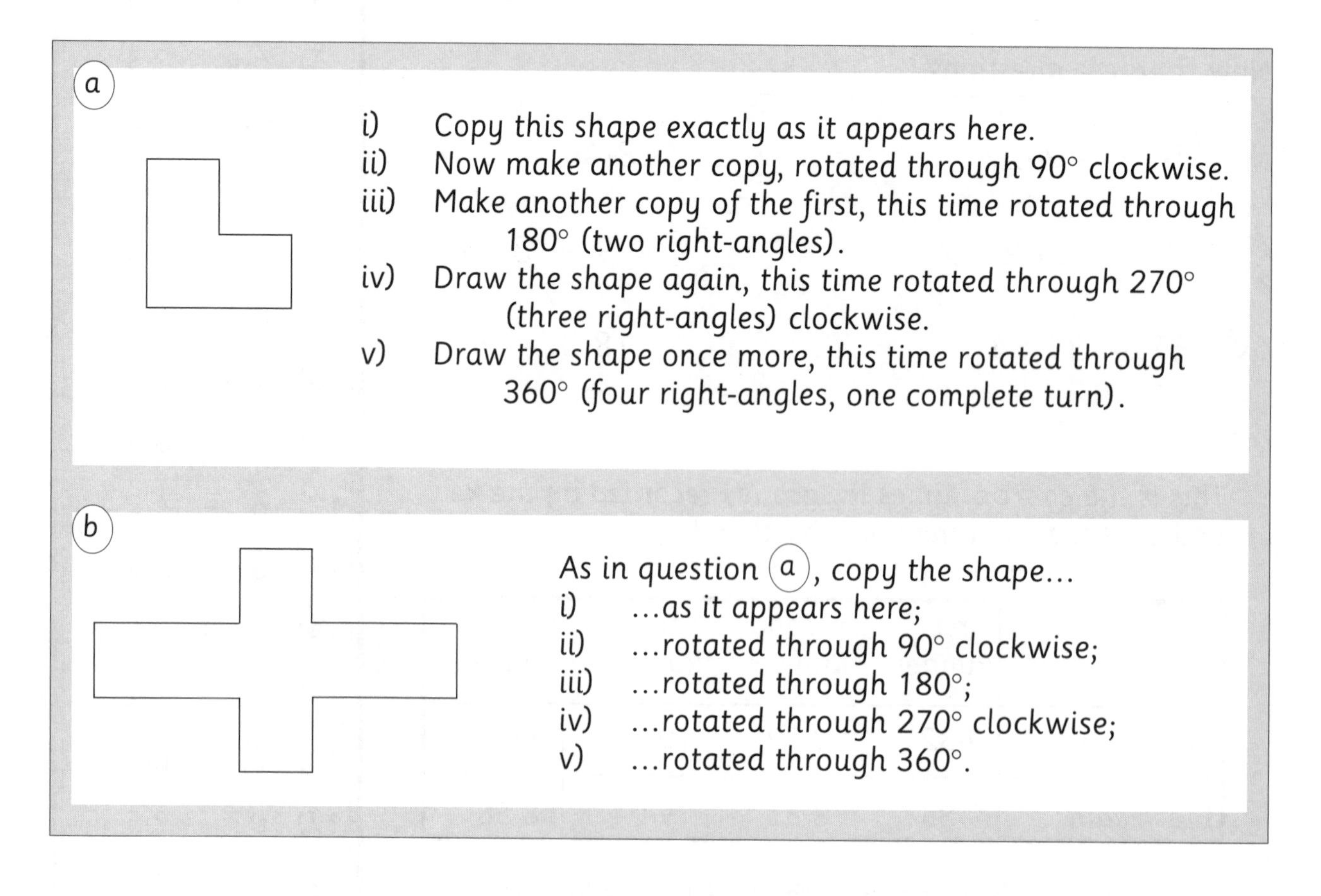

In question (b), the shape looked identical to the original shape, firstly when it was rotated through 180° and secondly when it was rotated through 360°.
We say that it has **rotational symmetry** of **order 2.**

In question (a), the shape looked identical to the original shape only when it was rotated through 360°. We say that it has **rotational symmetry** of **order 1.**

Grid paper

Rotational and Reflectional Symmetry

Look again at the shapes featured on page 10.

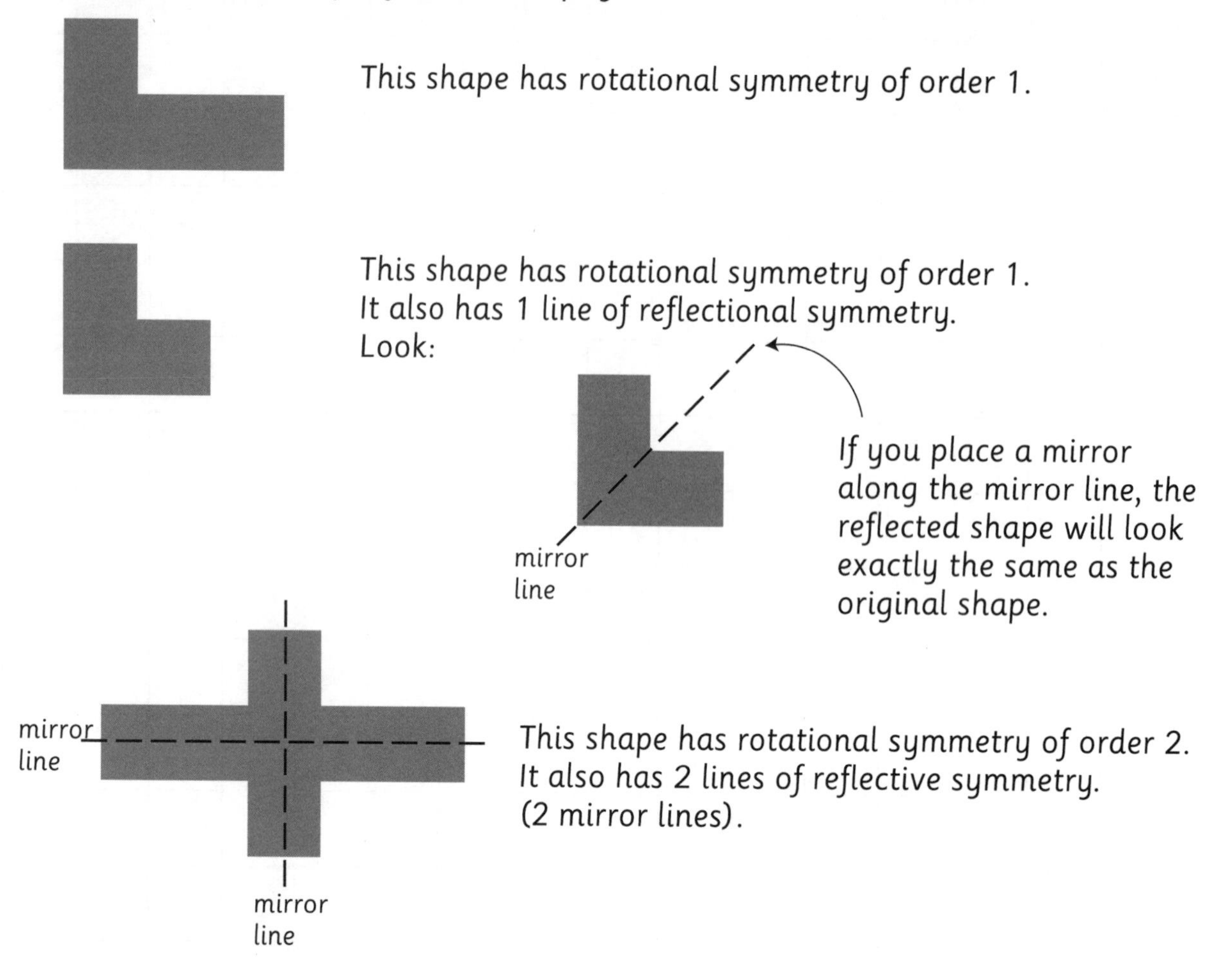

For each shape below, state the order of rotational symmetry and the number of lines of reflectional symmetry.

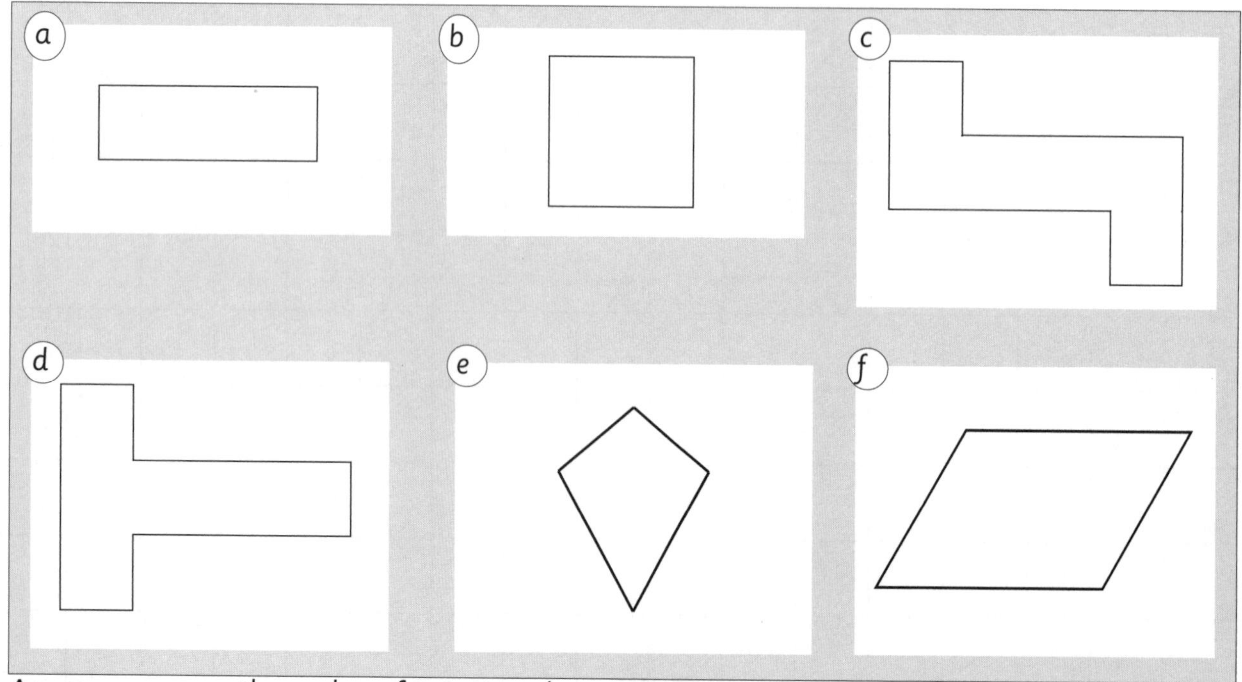

As you can see, the order of rotational symmetry is not always the same as the number of lines of reflective symmetry.

Triangles

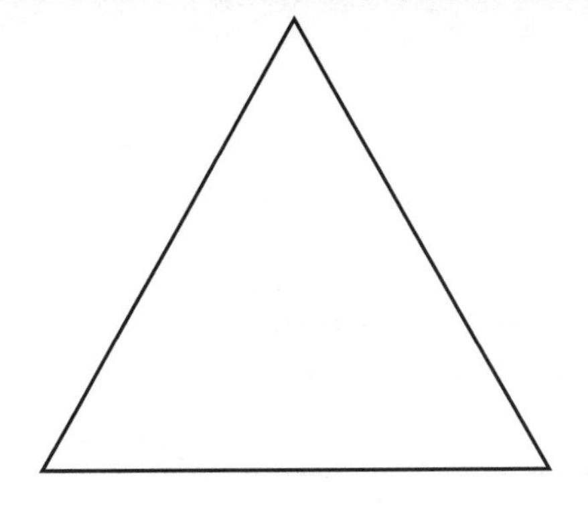

This is an equilateral triangle.
Its three sides are all the same length.
Its three angles are all equal.
It has rotational symmetry of order 3 (because if you could pick up a copy of it and turn it round, it would fit back into its own shape 3 times).

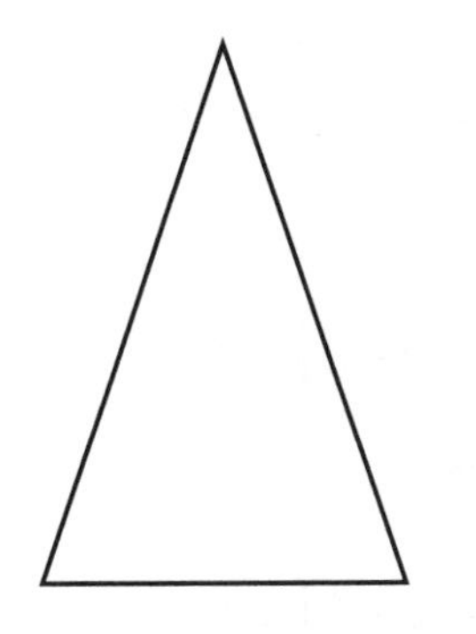

This is an isosceles triangle.
Two of its sides are equal in length.
Two of its angles are equal in size.

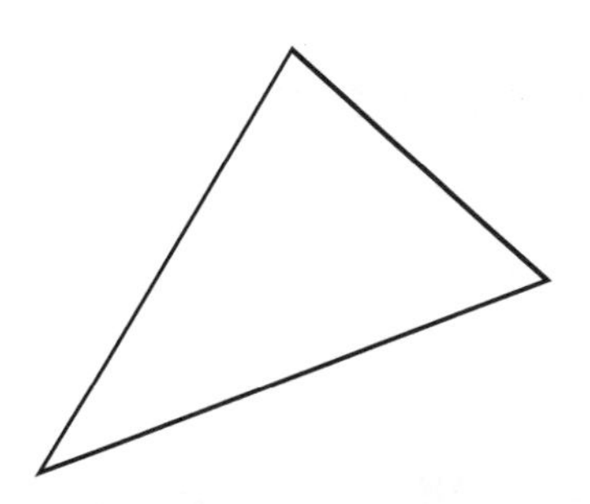

This is a scalene triangle.
All of its sides are different in length.
All of its angles are different in length.

(a) How many lines of reflectional symmetry does an equilateral triangle have?

(b) How many lines of reflectional symmetry does an isosceles triangle have?

(c) What order of rotational symmetry does an isosceles triangle have?

(d) How many lines of reflectional symmetry does a scalene triangle have?

(e) What order of rotational symmetry does a scalene triangle have?

Did you know that the three angles of a triangle always add up to 180°?

Multiples

1	x	2	=	2
2	x	2	=	4
3	x	2	=	6
4	x	2	=	8
5	x	2	=	10
6	x	2	=	12
7	x	2	=	14
8	x	2	=	16
9	x	2	=	18
10	x	2	=	20

All of these numbers are multiples of two.

Any number that can be exactly divided by 2 is a multiple of 2.

Answer these questions:

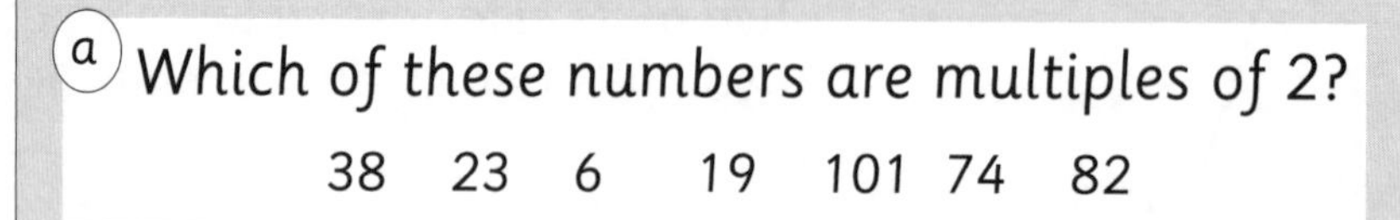

(a) Which of these numbers are multiples of 2?

38 23 6 19 101 74 82

(b) Which of these numbers are multiples of 3?

9 18 26 24 27 31 7

(c) Which of these numbers are multiples of 4?

17 16 24 32 41 29 36

These numbers are all multiples of 4:

4 8 12 16 20 24 28 32 36 40 44 48 52 56 60 ...

These numbers are all multiples of 6:

6 12 18 24 30 36 42 48 54 60 66 72 78 84 90 ...

(d) Which of the numbers on these lists are multiples of both 4 and 6?

The smallest number which is a multiple of both 4 and 6 is 12.

We say that 12 is the lowest common multiple of 4 and 6.

You need to know all the multiplication tables.

If you need to look at them, the tables are written inside the back cover of this book.

Use your multiplication tables to help you to answer these questions.

(a) What is the lowest common multiple of 3 and 7?

(b) What is the lowest common multiple of 6 and 8?

(c) What is the lowest common multiple of 6 and 9?

(d) What is the lowest common multiple of 10 and 4?

Answer these multiplication questions:

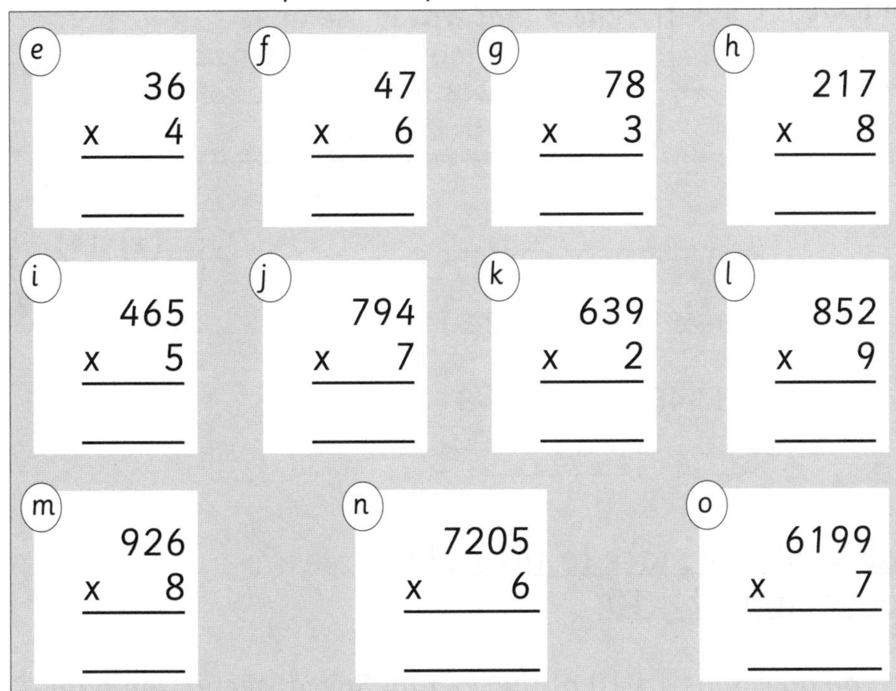

Mental Speed

Time yourself to see how quickly you can answer these questions in your head.

1) 63 ÷ 9
2) 48 ÷ 6
3) 36 ÷ 9
4) 20 ÷ 4
5) 64 ÷ 8
6) 72 ÷ 8
7) 54 ÷ 6
8) 21 ÷ 7
9) 48 ÷ 8
10) 24 ÷ 4
11) 35 ÷ 5
12) 32 ÷ 4
13) 54 ÷ 9
14) 42 ÷ 7
15) 30 ÷ 6
16) 25 ÷ 5
17) 16 ÷ 4
18) 9 ÷ 3
19) 36 ÷ 6
20) 49 ÷ 7

Time taken:

☐ seconds.

Multiplying by 10

6 x 10 = 60   10 x 6 = 60

When you multiply 6 by 10...

... the 6 that was in the units column moves to the tens column and we write a zero in the units.

Look at these examples:

7 x 10 = 70	24 x 10 = 240	365 x 10 = 3650

Try these questions:

(a) 8 x 10	(b) 18 x 10	(c) 28 x 10	(d) 76 x 10
(e) 49 x 10	(f) 613 x 10	(g) 1468 x 10	(h) 2842 x 10
(i) 60 x 10	(j) 400 x 10	(k) 3000 x 10	(l) 20000 x 10

Now look at this example: 3·6 x 10 = 36

Notice that we are not just putting a zero on the end...

...the 3 that was in the units column has moved to the tens and the 6 that was in the tenths column has moved to the units.

Here are some more examples:

6·25 x 10 = 62·5

37·48 x 10 = 374·8

A simple trick is to ...

<u>move the decimal point one place to the right when you multiply by 10.</u>

You can try this when you do questions 1 - 10 of the 'Mental Speed' section on page 17.

Dividing by 10

$40 \div 10 = 4$

When you divide 40 by 10...

...the 4 that was in the tens column moves to the units column.

Look at these examples:

$250 \div 10 = 25$ $1000 \div 10 = 100$

Try these questions:

(a) $70 \div 10$	(b) $320 \div 10$	(c) $640 \div 10$
(d) $80 \div 10$	(e) $1200 \div 10$	(f) $7850 \div 10$

Now look at this example: $24 \div 10 = 2{\cdot}4$

The 4 that was in the units has moved to the tenths...

...and the 2 that was in the tens has moved to the units.

A simple trick is to ...

<u>move the decimal point one place to the left when you divide by 10.</u>

You can try this when you do questions 11 - 20 of the 'Mental Speed' section on this page.

Mental Speed

Time yourself to see how quickly you can answer these questions in your head.

1) 34 x 10
2) 4·2 x 10
3) 2·65 x 10
4) 12·3 x 10
5) 21·04 x 10
6) 67·25 x 10
7) 3·194 x 10
8) 42·8 x 10
9) 72·9 x 10
10) 17·65 x 10
11) 480 ÷ 10
12) 56 ÷ 10
13) 38 ÷ 10
14) 17 ÷ 10
15) 6 ÷ 10
16) 4 ÷ 10
17) 8 ÷ 10
18) 3·2 ÷ 10
19) 2·4 ÷ 10
20) 9·7 ÷ 10

Time taken:

☐ seconds.

Multiplying by Multiples of Ten

Look at this example:

$$\begin{array}{r} 34 \\ \times\ 20 \\ \hline \\ \hline \end{array} \Rightarrow \begin{array}{r} 34 \\ \times\ 20 \\ \hline 0 \\ \hline \end{array} \Rightarrow \begin{array}{r} 34 \\ \times\ 20 \\ \hline 80 \\ \hline \end{array} \Rightarrow \begin{array}{r} 34 \\ \times\ 20 \\ \hline 680 \\ \hline \end{array}$$

Start by putting a zero in the units.

4 x 2 = 8

3 x 2 = 6

Here is another example:

$$\begin{array}{r} 76 \\ \times\ 40 \\ \hline \\ \hline \end{array} \Rightarrow \begin{array}{r} 76 \\ \times\ 40 \\ \hline 0 \\ \hline \end{array} \Rightarrow \begin{array}{r} 76 \\ \times\ 40 \\ \hline 40 \\ \hline {}_{2}\ \ \end{array} \Rightarrow \begin{array}{r} 76 \\ \times\ 40 \\ \hline 3040 \\ \hline {}_{2}\ \ \end{array}$$

zero in the units because we are multiplying by a multiple of ten.

6 x 4 = 24

7 x 4 = 28
28 + 2 = 30

Try these questions:

a) $\begin{array}{r} 28 \\ \times\ 30 \\ \hline \\ \hline \end{array}$ b) $\begin{array}{r} 46 \\ \times\ 70 \\ \hline \\ \hline \end{array}$ c) $\begin{array}{r} 58 \\ \times\ 20 \\ \hline \\ \hline \end{array}$ d) $\begin{array}{r} 39 \\ \times\ 60 \\ \hline \\ \hline \end{array}$ e) $\begin{array}{r} 62 \\ \times\ 40 \\ \hline \\ \hline \end{array}$

f) $\begin{array}{r} 93 \\ \times\ 80 \\ \hline \\ \hline \end{array}$ g) $\begin{array}{r} 87 \\ \times\ 50 \\ \hline \\ \hline \end{array}$ h) $\begin{array}{r} 76 \\ \times\ 90 \\ \hline \\ \hline \end{array}$ i) $\begin{array}{r} 59 \\ \times\ 30 \\ \hline \\ \hline \end{array}$ j) $\begin{array}{r} 64 \\ \times\ 60 \\ \hline \\ \hline \end{array}$

k) $\begin{array}{r} 217 \\ \times\ 20 \\ \hline \\ \hline \end{array}$ l) $\begin{array}{r} 429 \\ \times\ 70 \\ \hline \\ \hline \end{array}$ m) $\begin{array}{r} 594 \\ \times\ 30 \\ \hline \\ \hline \end{array}$ n) $\begin{array}{r} 708 \\ \times\ 40 \\ \hline \\ \hline \end{array}$

o) $\begin{array}{r} 899 \\ \times\ 50 \\ \hline \\ \hline \end{array}$ p) $\begin{array}{r} 910 \\ \times\ 60 \\ \hline \\ \hline \end{array}$ q) $\begin{array}{r} 600 \\ \times\ 70 \\ \hline \\ \hline \end{array}$ r) $\begin{array}{r} 3000 \\ \times\ 30 \\ \hline \\ \hline \end{array}$

Multiplying by Tens and Units

Here are the 23 bags of sweets:
Each bag contains 34 sweets.

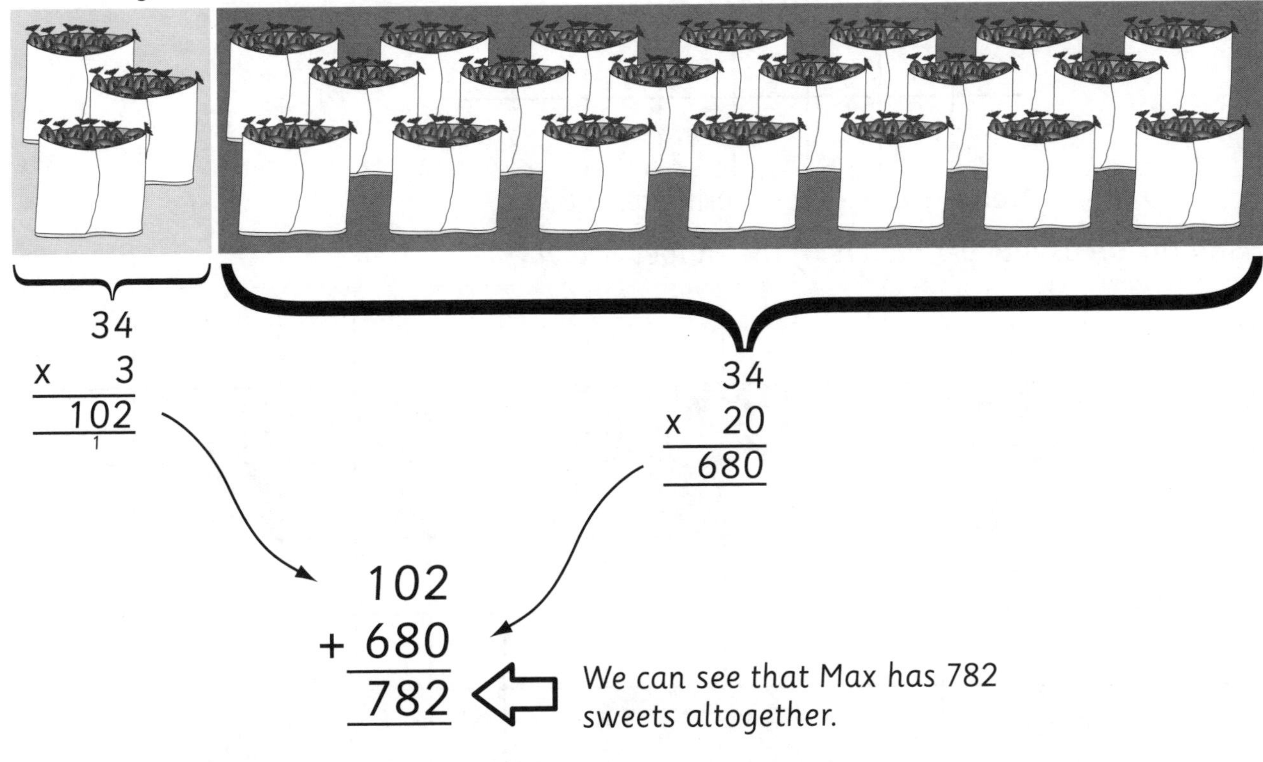

Here is a quicker way to work out the answer:

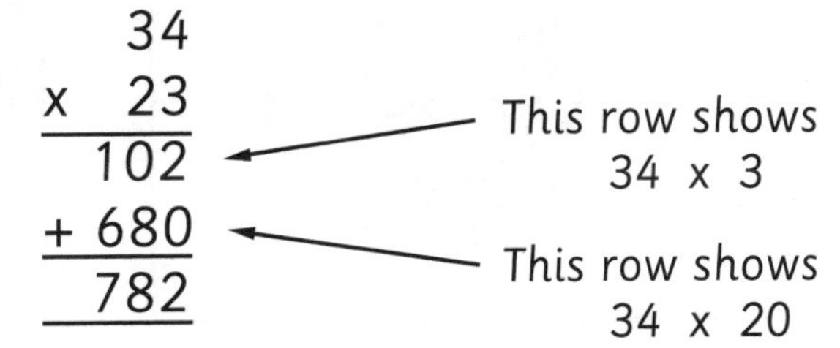

Try the questions below:
Don't forget to put a zero in the units column when you multiply by a multiple of ten.

a	b	c	d	e
48	56	83	78	69
x 27	x 32	x 16	x 41	x 58
+	+	+	+	+

Area and Perimeter

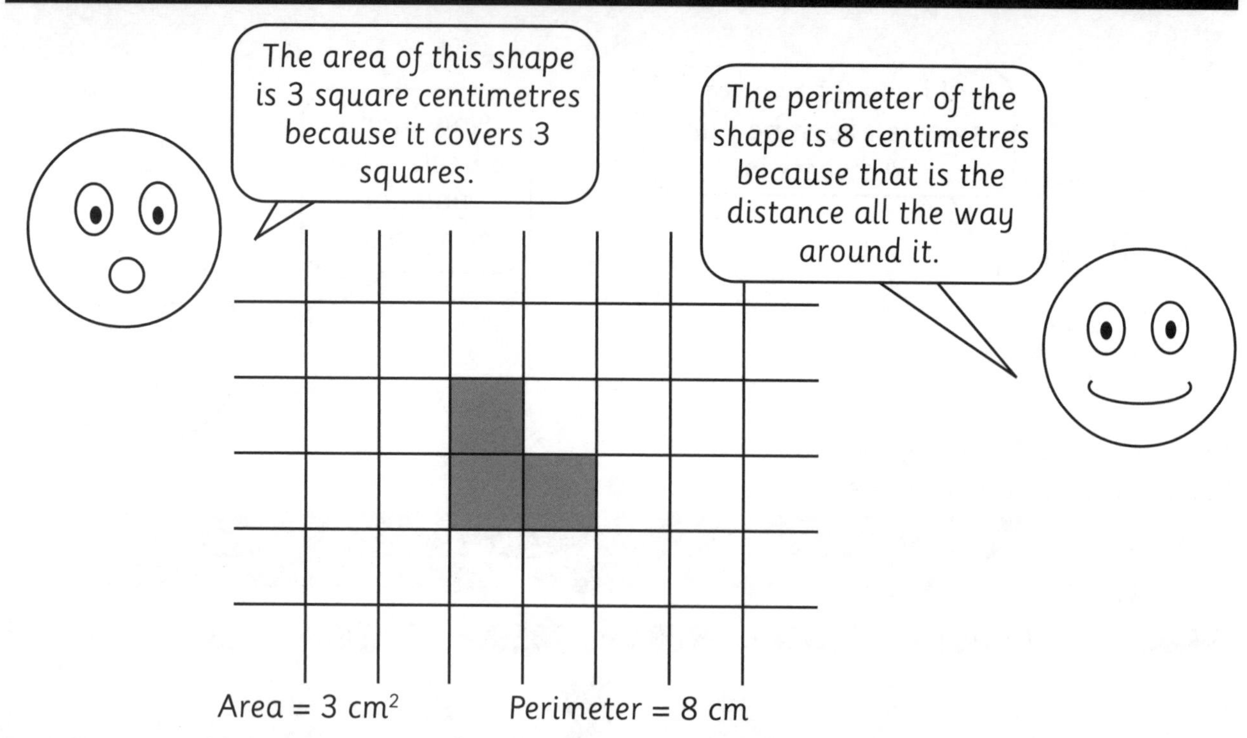

Area = 3 cm² Perimeter = 8 cm

Find the areas and perimeters of the shapes below.

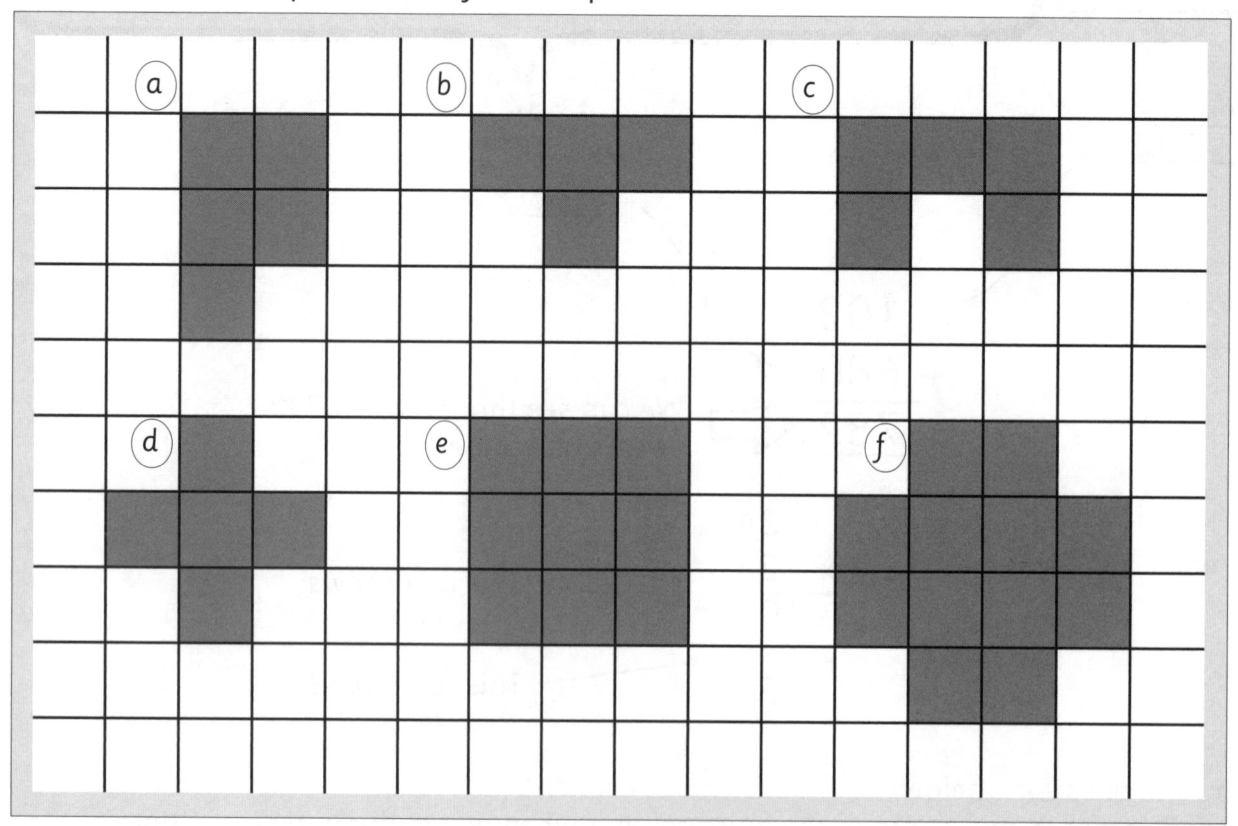

For questions (g) and (h) you need some grid paper.

(g) Draw three different shapes with area of 4 cm²

(h) Find the perimeters of your 3 shapes.
Are they the same for each one?

Maths Today for ages 10 -11
Removable Answer Section

Page 2 *a* 54 *b* 70 *c* 97 *d* 104 *e* 101 *f* 372 *g* 606 *h* 750 *i* 939 *j* 691
k 107 *l* 84 *m* 170 *n* 134 *o* 249 *p* 661 *q* 848 *r* 952 *s* 825 *t* 857 *u* 1472

Page 3 *a* 3055 *b* 7812 *c* 2719 *d* 4758 *e* 41690 *f* 69581 *g* 251462 *h* 861300 *i* 6108113

Mental *1* 60 *2* 50 *3* 80 *4* 100 *5* 100 *6* 90 *7* 60 *8* 40 *9* 100 *10* 90
Speed *11* 32 *12* 38 *13* 28 *14* 24 *15* 36 *16* 26 *17* 34 *18* 30 *19* 70 *20* 90

Page 4 *a* 26 *b* 38 *c* 42 *d* 36 *e* 32 *f* 57 *g* 204 *h* 332 *i* 385 *j* 391
k 569 *l* 586 *m* 312 *n* 208 *o* 518 *p* 777 *q* 352 *r* 278

Page 5 *a* 2541 *b* 4641 *c* 1827 *d* 5486 *e* 5923 *f* 3337 *g* 15540 *h* 37064 *i* 25381 *j* 75000
k £6·55 *l* £18·04 *m* £26·52 *n* £55·05 *o* £12·50 *p* £45·28

Mental *1* 82 *2* 75 *3* 54 *4* 46 *5* 18 *6* 9 *7* 61 *8* 23 *9* 37 *10* 25
Speed *11* 72 *12* 55 *13* 24 *14* 26 *15* 37 *16* 23 *17* 25 *18* 475 *19* 725 *20* 550

Page 6 *a* 5·7 *b* 8·9 *c* 9·4 *d* 6·7 *e* 8·4 *f* 18·1 *g* 30·1

Page 7 *a* 25·65 *b* 23·43 *c* 27 *d* 35·19 *e* 145·77 *f* 100 *g (i)* 36·93 *(ii)* 36·26 *(iii)* Blue team
Mental *1* 9·3 *2* 7·8 *3* 3·8 *4* 6·8 *5* 10·9 *6* 12·9 *7* 15·9 *8* 11·7 *9* 11·9 *10* 7·7
Speed *11* 6·3 *12* 8·7 *13* 7·6 *14* 10·1 *15* 6 *16* 13·4 *17* 13 *18* 13·6 *19* 1 *20* 0·5

Page 8 *a* 4·3 *b* 6·2 *c* 4·3 *d* 5·1 *e* 6·7 *f* 10·1 *g* 11·7 *h* 27·7 *i* 57·8 *j* 66·9
k 133·5 *l* 218·6 *m* 30·2 *n* 36·3

Page 9 *a* 3·12 *b* 1·48 *c* 10·38 *d* 6·25 *e* 35·36 *f* 8·57

g (i) The third runner *(ii)* The first runner *(iii)* 1·18 seconds

Mental *1* 3·2 *2* 3 *3* 6·8 *4* 2·9 *5* 4·1 *6* 6 *7* 2·3 *8* 1·1 *9* 4·2 *10* 0·9
Speed *11* 1·2 *12* 1·8 *13* 2·8 *14* 3·8 *15* 4·8 *16* 5·8 *17* 2·5 *18* 7·5 *19* 3·9 *20* 1·3

Page 10 *a (i)* *(ii)* *(iii)* *(iv)* *(v)*

b (i) *(ii)* *(iii)* *(iv)* *(v)*

Page 12
a rotational symmetry of order 2; 2 lines of reflective symmetry
b rotational symmetry of order 4; 4 lines of reflective symmetry
c rotational symmetry of order 2; 0 lines of reflective symmetry
d rotational symmetry of order 1; 1 line of reflective symmetry
e rotational symmetry of order 1; 1 line of reflective symmetry
f rotational symmetry of order 2; 0 lines of reflective symmetry

Page 13 *a* 3 *b* 1 *c* 1 *d* 0 *e* 1

Page 14 *a* 38, 6, 74, 82 *b* 9, 18, 24, 27, *c* 16, 24, 32, 36 *d* 12, 24, 36, 48, 60

Page 15 *a* 21 *b* 24 *c* 18 *d* 20 *e* 144 *f* 282 *g* 234 *h* 1736 *i* 2325 *j* 5558
k 1278 *l* 7668 *m* 7408 *n* 43230 *o* 43393

Mental *1* 7 *2* 8 *3* 4 *4* 5 *5* 8 *6* 9 *7* 9 *8* 3 *9* 6 *10* 6
Speed *11* 7 *12* 8 *13* 6 *14* 6 *15* 5 *16* 5 *17* 4 *18* 3 *19* 6 *20* 7

Page 16 *a* 80 *b* 180 *c* 280 *d* 760 *e* 490 *f* 6130 *g* 14680 *h* 28420 *i* 600
j 4000 *k* 30000 *l* 200000

Page 17 *a* 7 *b* 32 *c* 64 *d* 8 *e* 120 *f* 785

Mental *1* 340 *2* 42 *3* 26·5 *4* 123 *5* 210·4 *6* 672·5 *7* 31·94 *8* 428 *9* 729 *10* 176·5
Speed *11* 48 *12* 5·6 *13* 3·8 *14* 1·7 *15* 0·6 *16* 0·4 *17* 0·8 *18* 0·32 *19* 0·24 *20* 0·97

Page 18 *a* 840 *b* 3220 *c* 1160 *d* 2340 *e* 2480 *f* 7440 *g* 4350 *h* 6840 *i* 1770 *j* 3840
k 4340 *l* 30030 *m* 17820 *n* 28320 *o* 44950 *p* 54600 *q* 42000 *r* 90000

Page 19 *a* 1296 *b* 1792 *c* 1328 *d* 3198 *e* 4002

Page 20 *a* area = 5cm² perimeter = 10cm *b* area = 4cm² perimeter = 10cm

c area = 5cm² perimeter = 12cm *d* area = 5cm² perimeter = 12cm

e area = 9cm² perimeter = 12cm *f* area = 12cm² perimeter = 16cm

g and h answers depend on shapes drawn by pupil

Page 21
a area is in the range of 30cm² to 36cm² (any answer between these is acceptable)
b area is in the range of 10cm² to 14cm²
c area is in the range of 15cm² to 23cm²

Mental *1* 74p *2* 52p *3* 18p *4* 4p *5* 83p *6* 97p *7* 49p *8* 26p *9* 31p *10* 65p
Speed *11* £2·10 *12* £3·40 *13* £1·80 *14* 20p *15* £2·50
16 £3·25 *17* £1·75 *18* £3·04 *19* £1·96 *20* £2·33

Page 22
a sides = 3cm and 4cm area = 12cm²
b sides = 2cm and 5cm area = 10cm²
c sides = 4cm and 6cm area = 24cm²

Page 23 *a* This rectangle has sides of 2·7cm and 3·4cm so its area is 9·18cm^2
b This rectangle has sides of 4·7cm and 6·3cm so its area is 29·61cm^2

Mental *1* 2 *2* 3 *3* 4 *4* $3\frac{1}{2}$ *5* 5 *6* 10 *7* $7\frac{1}{2}$ *8* $12\frac{1}{2}$ *9* 16 *10* 25

Speed *11* 24 *12* 26 *13* 32 *14* 50 *15* 75 *16* 500 *17* 250 *18* 750 *19* 125 *20* 350

Page 24 *a* 2cm^3 *b* 3cm^3 *c* 8cm^3 *d* 12cm^3 *e* 5cm^3

Page 25 *a* 24cm^3 *b* 30cm^3 *c* 16cm^3 *d* 8cm^3 *e* 27cm^3 *f* 64cm^3

Mental *1* 2 *2* 3 *3* 1 *4* $1\frac{1}{2}$ *5* $2\frac{1}{2}$ *6* 5 *7* 25 *8* 250 *9* 10 *10* 20

Speed *11* $7\frac{1}{2}$ *12* $12\frac{1}{2}$ *13* 50 *14* 75 *15* 100 *16* 125 *17* 150 *18* 175 *19* 200 *20* 225

Page 26 *a* £8 *b* £3·50 *c* 30p *d* 35kg *e* £500 *f* £2 *g* £5 *h* 20m *i* £1·50 *j* 4·5km
k £24 *l* 30 miles *m* 150 children *n* 21 videos

Page 27 *a* 4 sweets *b* 7 litres *c* £6 *d* £25 *e* 30p *f* 50 centimetres
g 8 *h* 42 *i* 6 *j* £160 *k* £75 *l* £450
m 30p *n* £1·80 *o* £3·20 *p* £1·32 *q* £1·62 *r* £11·20 *s* £20 *t* £3·80 *u* £4 *v* £6·75

Mental *1* 4 *2* 12 *3* 5 *4* 15 *5* 10 *6* 30 *7* 2 *8* 6 *9* 3 *10* 9

Speed *11* 7 *12* 21 *13* 9 *14* 27 *15* 6 *16* 18 *17* 8 *18* 24 *19* 25 *20* 75

Page 28 *b* 0·3 *c* 60% = 0·6 *d* 80% = 0·8 *e* 90% = 0·9 *f* 0·4

Page 29

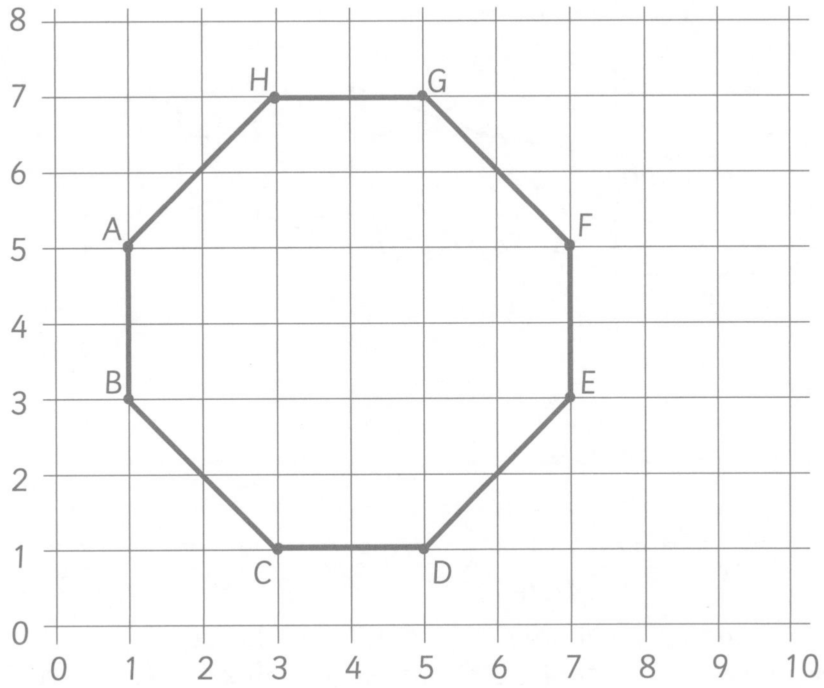

Coordinates:

B (1,3)
C (3,1)
D (5,1)
E (7,3)
F (7,5)
G (5,7)

H (3,7)

Page 30 *a* 20 *b* 60 *c* 15 *d* 35 *e* 70 *f* 52 *g* 8 *h* 26 *i* 4·5 *j* 10 *k* 120 *l* 17
m 200 *n* 400 *o* 3 *p* 2000 *q* 3000 *r* 250 *s* 610 *t* 6100
u 3000 *v* 3500 *w* 2500 *x* 1·5 *y* 4·5 *z* 0·6 *A* 4100 *B* 2·9

Page 31 *a* 10 *b* 800ml *c* 5 *d* 20
e 1l 200ml 1200ml *f* 2l 700ml 2700ml
g 3·3l 3300ml *h* 4·6l 4l 600ml *i* 0·009l *j* 0·039l *k* 0·602l *l* 1·674l
Mental *1* 12 *2* 22 *3* 40 *4* 32 *5* 10 *6* 26 *7* 38 *8* 16 *9* 28 *10* 24
Speed *11* 34 *12* 18 *13* 42 *14* 46 *15* 50 *16* 100 *17* 150 *18* 160 *19* 58 *20* 122

Page 32 *a* 7 *b* 6 *c* 9 *d* 12 *e* 8 r3 *f* 4 r3 *g* 25 *h* 24 *i* 39 *j* 29
k 72 r3 *l* 206 *m* 148 r2 *n* 454 r1 *o* 58 *p* 61 r5 *q* 112 r4 *r* 66 r4

Page 33 *a* 20·5 *b* 9·5 *c* 12·75 *d* 33·5 *e* 36·5 *f* 9·8 *g* 11·375 *h* 35·25 *i* 12·5
j 23·4 *k* 62·5 *l* 62·5
Mental *1* 24 *2* 11 *3* 58 *4* 37 *5* 25 *6* 175 *7* 325 *8* 259 *9* 487 *10* 387
Speed *11* 249 *12* 259 *13* 481 *14* 613 *15* 500 *16* 0·8 *17* 0·4 *18* 5·4 *19* 2·8 *20* 7·9

Page 34 *a* 4·7 *b* 9·9 *c* 8·3 *d* 3·9 *e* 6·32 *f* 7·45 *g* 9·78
h 12·59 *i* 4·74 *j* 23·45 *k* 6·35 *l* 4·925

Page 35 *a* 25 *b* 36 *c* 49 *d* 64 *e* 81 *f* 100 *g* 225 *h* 625 *i* 289 *j* 400
k 196 *l* 121 *m* 361 *n* 900 *o* 169 *p* 2500 *q* 144 *r* 324 *s* 1600 *t* 3600 *u* 4096
Mental *1* 18 *2* 46 *3* 63 *4* 71 *5* 83 *6* 1 *7* 80 *8* 60 *9* 90 *10* 70
Speed *11* 80 *12* 100 *13* 110 *14* 120 *15* 150 *16* 175 *17* 125 *18* 175 *19* 375 *20* 525

Page 36 *a* 3° *b* 23° *c* 22° *d* 22°

Page 37 *a* ⁻2°C *b* 6°C *c* 8°C *d* 0°C *e* ⁻2° 0° 0° 1° 4° 5° 6° *f* 1°C *g* 2°C *h* 20°

Page 38 *a*

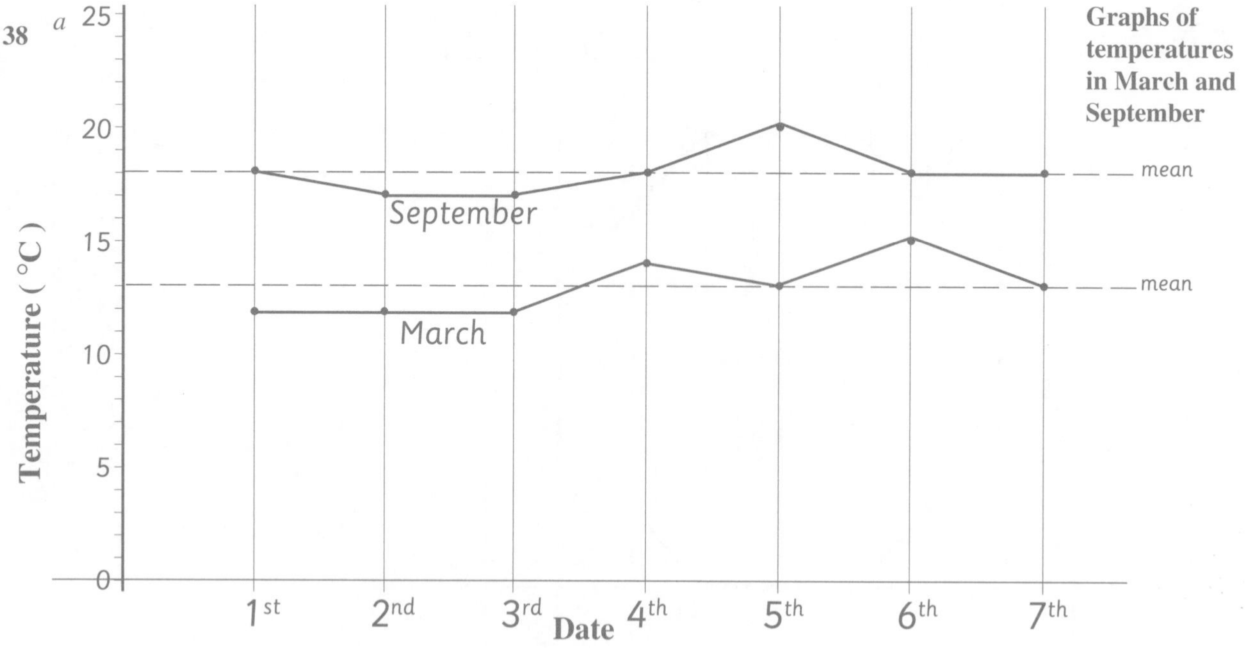

Graphs of temperatures in March and September

Temperature (°C): 0, 5, 10, 15, 20, 25
Date: 1st, 2nd, 3rd, 4th, 5th, 6th, 7th
September
March
mean
mean

Page 39 *a* yes *b* 6 hours *c* Minnie *d* Minnie *e* Max *f* Minnie
g between 3 and 5 hours *h* about 2 hours *i* 90° *j* 135°
Mental *1* 42 *2* 7 *3* 37 *4* 200 *5* 36 *6* 5·6 *7* 64 *8* 9 *9* 4 *10* 64
Speed *11* 0·8 *12* 230 *13* 2·3 *14* 51·2 *15* 49 *16* 13 *17* 8 *18* 2·8 *19* 325 *20* 175

Page 40 *a* one in six or $\frac{1}{6}$ *b* one in six or $\frac{1}{6}$ *c* three in six or $\frac{3}{6}$ or $\frac{1}{2}$
d one in five or $\frac{1}{5}$ *e* picking out a letter 'b' *f* certain *g* impossible
h unlikely *i* likely

Area of irregular shapes

It is not easy to find the area of an irregular shape. There are various ways to find an approximate area. Try the method described by Max and Minnie to estimate the areas of the shapes below.

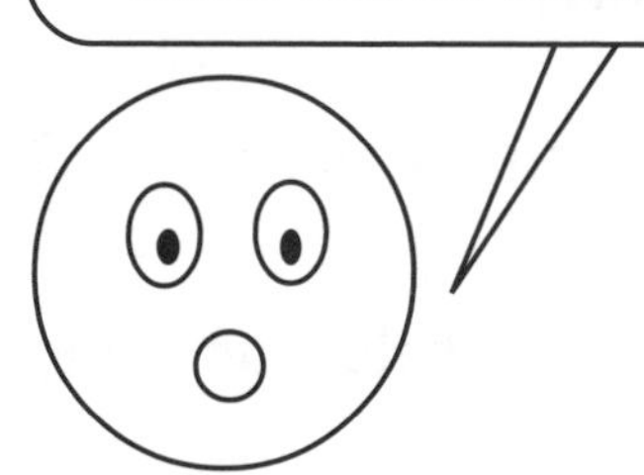

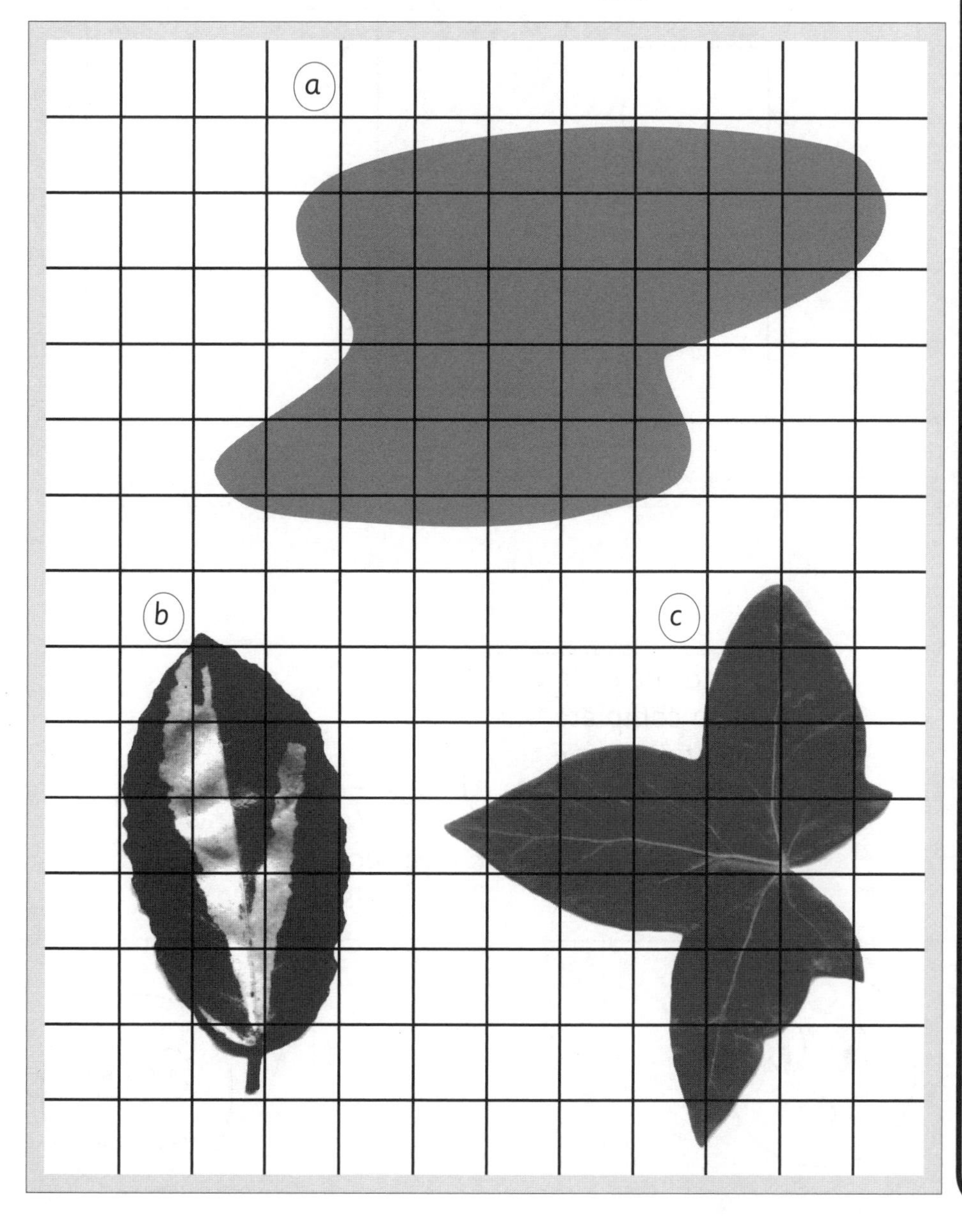

Mental Speed

Time yourself to see how quickly you can answer these questions in your head.

1) £1 – 26p
2) £1 – 48p
3) £1 – 82p
4) £1 – 96p
5) £1 – 17p
6) £1 – 3p
7) £1 – 51p
8) £1 – 74p
9) £1 – 69p
10) £1 – 35p
11) £5 – £2·90
12) £5 – £1·60
13) £5 – £3·20
14) £5 – £4·80
15) £5 – £2·50
16) £5 – £1·75
17) £5 – £3·25
18) £5 – £1·96
19) £5 – £3·04
20) £5 – £2·67

Time taken:

☐ seconds.

Areas of Rectangles

Look at this rectangle:

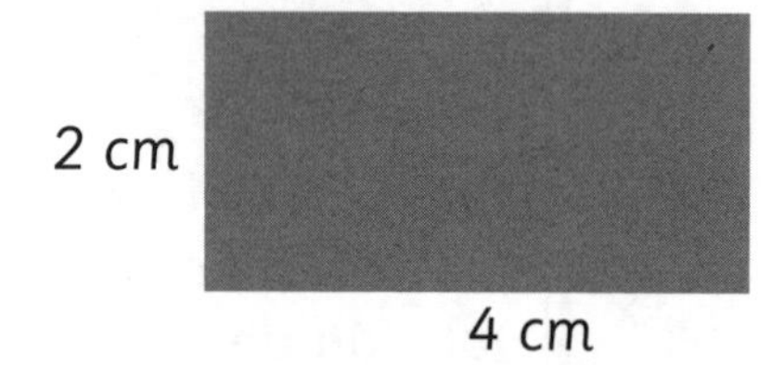

Because it is 2 cm wide and 4 cm long, it covers up 8 cm²

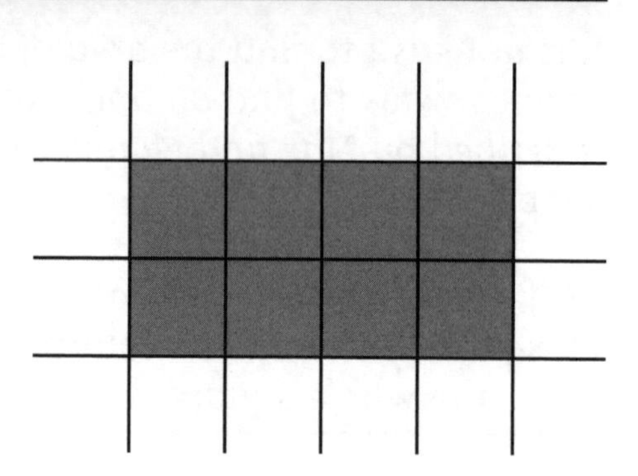

...so you can see that to find the area of a rectangle, you can multiply its width and its length together:

$$2 \text{ cm} \times 4 \text{ cm} = 8 \text{ cm}^2$$

Measure the sides of the rectangles below and calculate the area for each one.

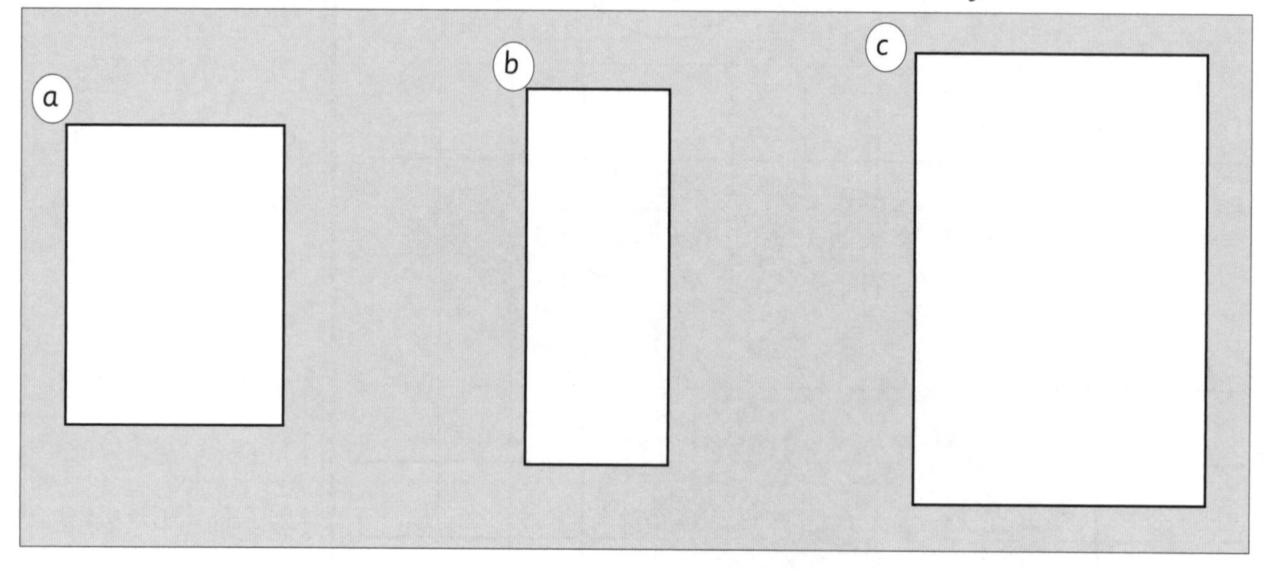

Look at this rectangle:

Step 1: Look carefully at the numbers.

4·2 x 3·4

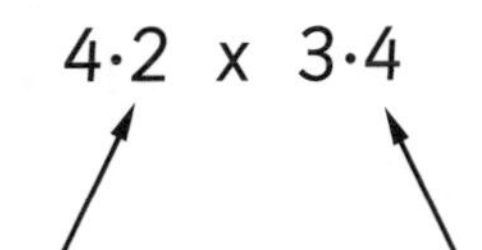

This number has one digit to the right of the decimal point so we say it has one decimal place.

This number also has one decimal place.

...so we have two decimal places altogether.

Step 2: Multiply:

```
   42  <- Notice that we have written
x  34  <- the numbers without the
 ----     decimal points.
  168
+1260
 ----
 1428
```

Step 3: Because we found two decimal places altogether in our starting numbers, we are going to put a decimal point into our answer to make it have two decimal places.

14·28

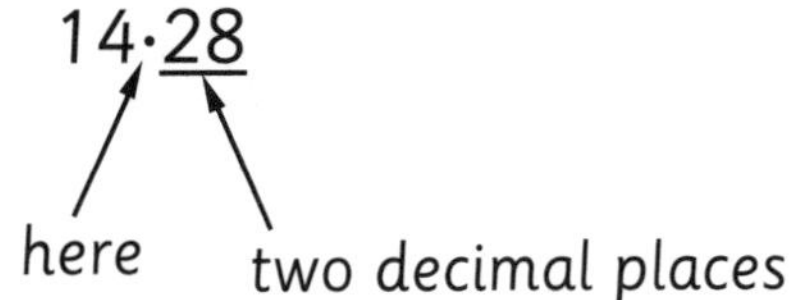

the decimal point goes here   two decimal places

The area of the rectangle at the bottom of page 22 is 14·28 cm^2.

Try finding the areas of these rectangles, using the method shown in the 3 steps above.

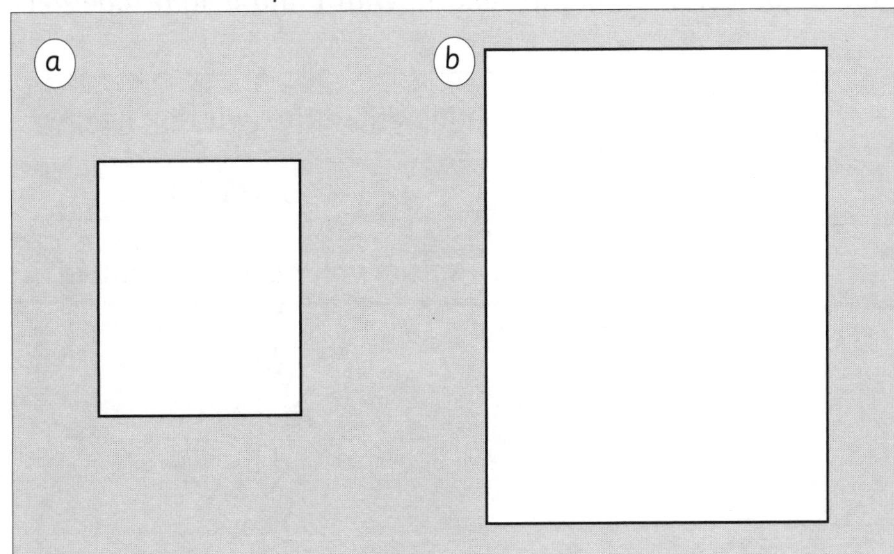

Mental Speed

Time yourself to see how quickly you can answer these questions in your head.

1) $\frac{1}{2}$ of 4
2) $\frac{1}{2}$ of 6
3) $\frac{1}{2}$ of 8
4) $\frac{1}{2}$ of 7
5) $\frac{1}{2}$ of 10
6) $\frac{1}{2}$ of 20
7) $\frac{1}{2}$ of 15
8) $\frac{1}{2}$ of 25
9) $\frac{1}{2}$ of 32
10) $\frac{1}{2}$ of 50
11) $\frac{1}{2}$ of 48
12) $\frac{1}{2}$ of 52
13) $\frac{1}{2}$ of 64
14) $\frac{1}{2}$ of 100
15) $\frac{1}{2}$ of 150
16) $\frac{1}{2}$ of 1000
17) $\frac{1}{2}$ of 500
18) $\frac{1}{2}$ of 1500
19) $\frac{1}{2}$ of 250
20) $\frac{1}{2}$ of 700

Time taken:

☐ seconds.

Volume

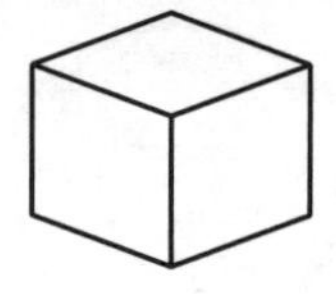

This is a picture of a cube.
Each edge of this cube is
one centimetre long.

We say that the cube has a volume of one cubic centimetre.

One cubic centimetre can be written like this: $1\ cm^3$

What is the volume of each of the shapes in the pictures below:

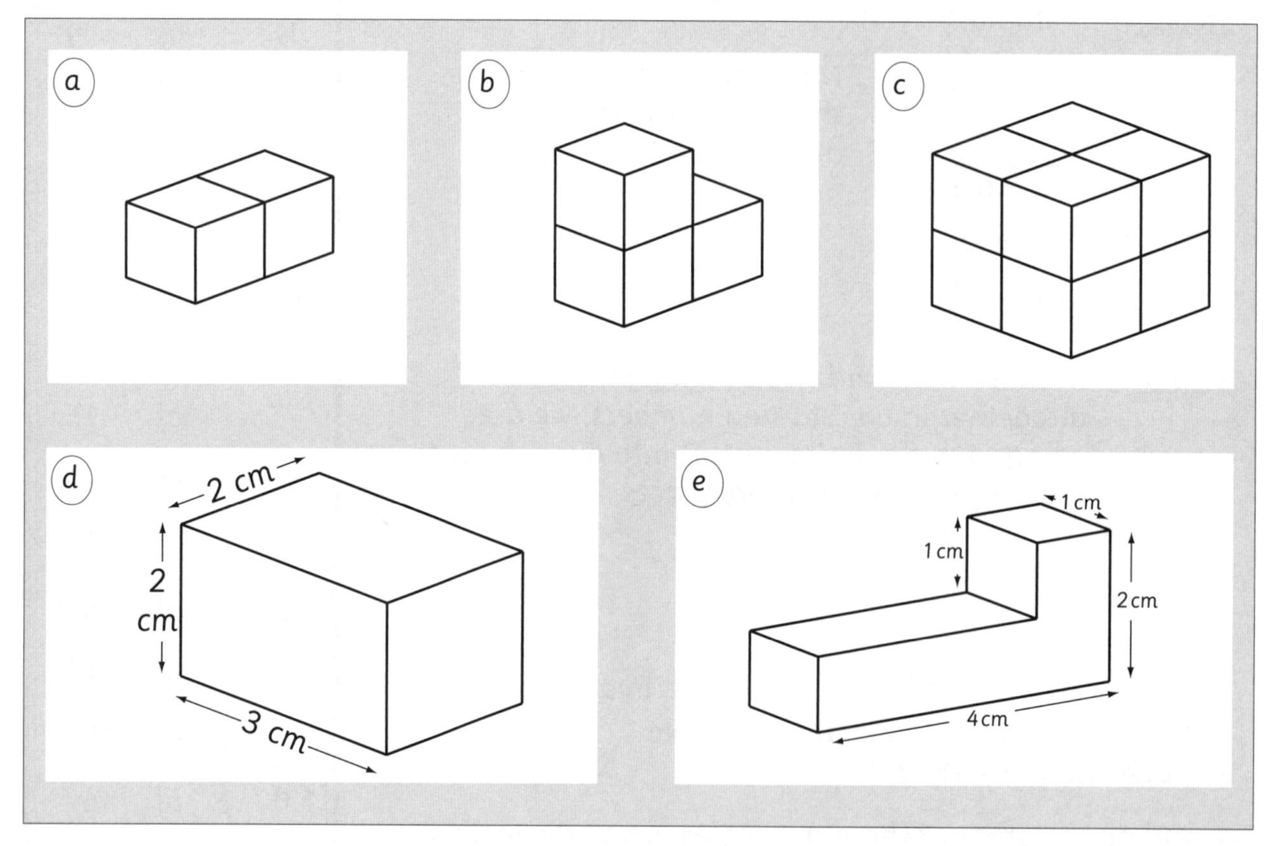

To find the volume of a cuboid you can multiply its length, width and height together.
Look at this example:

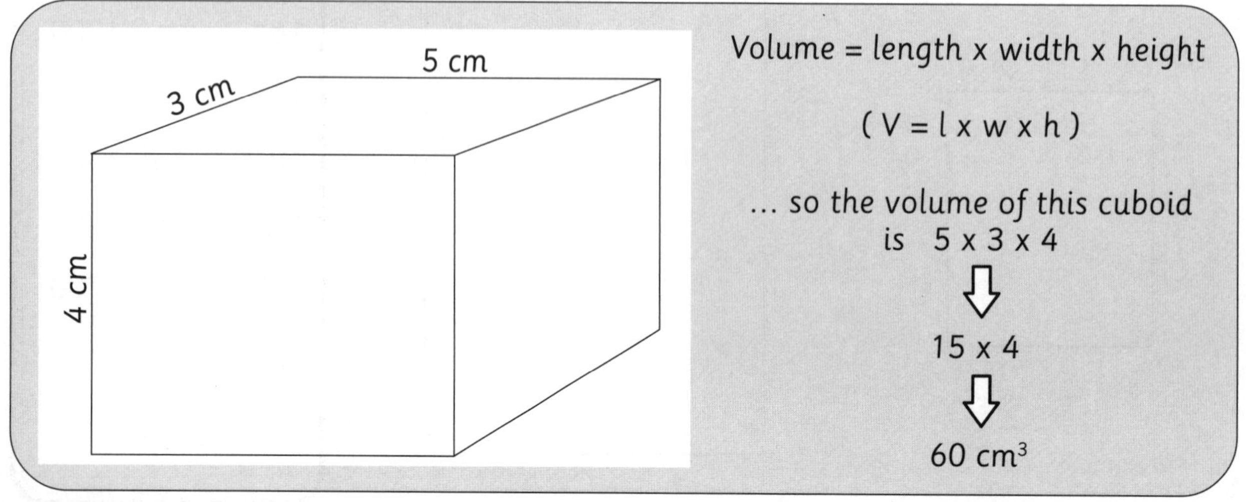

Find the volumes of these cuboids:

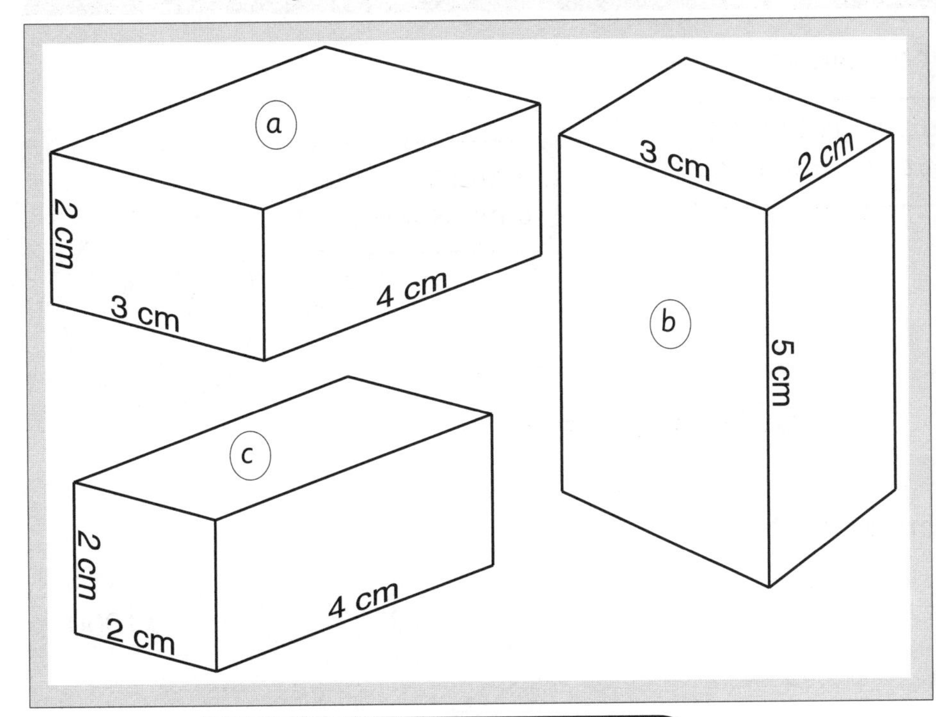

Cubes are special because all their edges are equal in length ...

... but the same method works.

Find the volumes of these cubes:

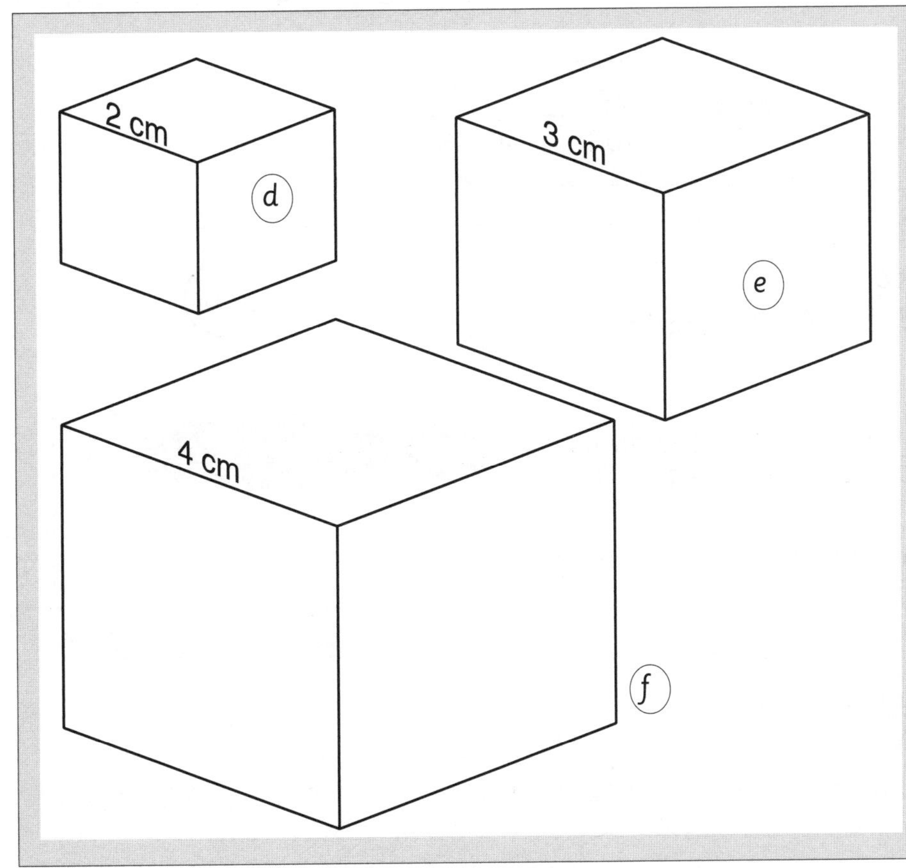

Mental Speed

Time yourself to see how quickly you can answer these questions in your head.

1) $\frac{1}{4}$ of 8

2) $\frac{1}{4}$ of 12

3) $\frac{1}{4}$ of 4

4) $\frac{1}{4}$ of 6

5) $\frac{1}{4}$ of 10

6) $\frac{1}{4}$ of 20

7) $\frac{1}{4}$ of 100

8) $\frac{1}{4}$ of 1000

9) $\frac{1}{4}$ of 40

10) $\frac{1}{4}$ of 80

11) $\frac{1}{4}$ of 30

12) $\frac{1}{4}$ of 50

13) $\frac{1}{4}$ of 200

14) $\frac{1}{4}$ of 300

15) $\frac{1}{4}$ of 400

16) $\frac{1}{4}$ of 500

17) $\frac{1}{4}$ of 600

18) $\frac{1}{4}$ of 700

19) $\frac{1}{4}$ of 800

20) $\frac{1}{4}$ of 900

Time taken:

☐ seconds.

Percentages

Per cent means 'out of a hundred'.

So fifty per cent means fifty out of a hundred.

...and that's the same as a half.

$$50\% = \frac{50}{100} = \frac{1}{2}$$

Find 50% of the following amounts:

a) £16 £8   b) £7 £3·50   c) 60p 30p   d) 70kg 35kg   e) £1000 £500

$$25\% = \frac{25}{100} = \frac{1}{4}$$

Find 25% of the following amounts:

f) £8 £2   g) £20 £5   h) 80 metres 20 metres   i) £6 £1:50   j) 18 kilometres $4\frac{1}{2}$k

$$75\% = \frac{75}{100} = \frac{3}{4}$$

Look at this example:

Find 75% of 20 kg

<u>Step 1:</u> Split the 20 into quarters...

20 → 5 5 5 5

<u>Step 2:</u> Add together 3 of the quarters...
5 + 5 + 5 = 15

... so 75% of 20 kg = 15 kg.

Find 75% of the following amounts:

k) £32 £24   l) 40 miles 30 miles   m) 200 children 150 children   n) 28 videos 21 videos

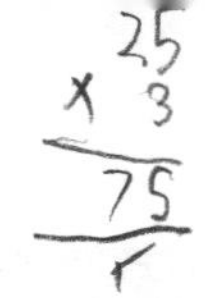

To find 10% of an amount …

…all you have to do is divide by ten.

Find 10% of the following amounts:

(a) 40 sweets	(b) 70 litres	(c) £60	(d) £250
(e) £3·00	(f) 5 metres (Clue: change the metres to centimetres first)		

To find 20%: first find 10% then multiply by 2.
To find 30%: first find 10% then multiply by 3.
To find 40%: first find 10% then multiply by 4.
To find 60%: first find 10% then multiply by 6.
To find 70%: first find 10% then multiply by 7.
To find 80%: first find 10% then multiply by 8.
To find 90%: first find 10% then multiply by 9.

Try these questions:

(g) 40% of 20	(h) 70% of 60	(i) 20% of 30
(j) 80% of £200	(k) 30% of £250	(l) 90% of £500

In the questions below, you might find it easier to change each amount to pence first.

(m) 20% of £1·50	(n) 30% of £6	(o) 40% of £8
(p) 50% of £2·64	(Don't forget: 50% is an easy percentage to find. You might wish to look back at page 26.)	
(q) 60% of £2·70	(r) 70% of £16	(s) 80% of £25
(t) 40% of £9·50	(u) 25% of £16	(v) 75% of £9

Look back at page 26 to remember how to find 25% and 75%.

Mental Speed

Time yourself to see how quickly you can answer these questions in your head.

1) $\frac{1}{4}$ of 16
2) $\frac{3}{4}$ of 16
3) $\frac{1}{4}$ of 20
4) $\frac{3}{4}$ of 20
5) $\frac{1}{4}$ of 40
6) $\frac{3}{4}$ of 40
7) $\frac{1}{4}$ of 8
8) $\frac{3}{4}$ of 8
9) $\frac{1}{4}$ of 12
10) $\frac{3}{4}$ of 12
11) $\frac{1}{4}$ of 28
12) $\frac{3}{4}$ of 28
13) $\frac{1}{4}$ of 36
14) $\frac{3}{4}$ of 36
15) $\frac{1}{4}$ of 24
16) $\frac{3}{4}$ of 24
17) $\frac{1}{4}$ of 32
18) $\frac{3}{4}$ of 32
19) $\frac{1}{4}$ of 100
20) $\frac{3}{4}$ of 100

Time taken:

[ ] seconds.

Fractions, Percentages and Decimals

Imagine that this is a cake which has been cut into ten equal pieces:

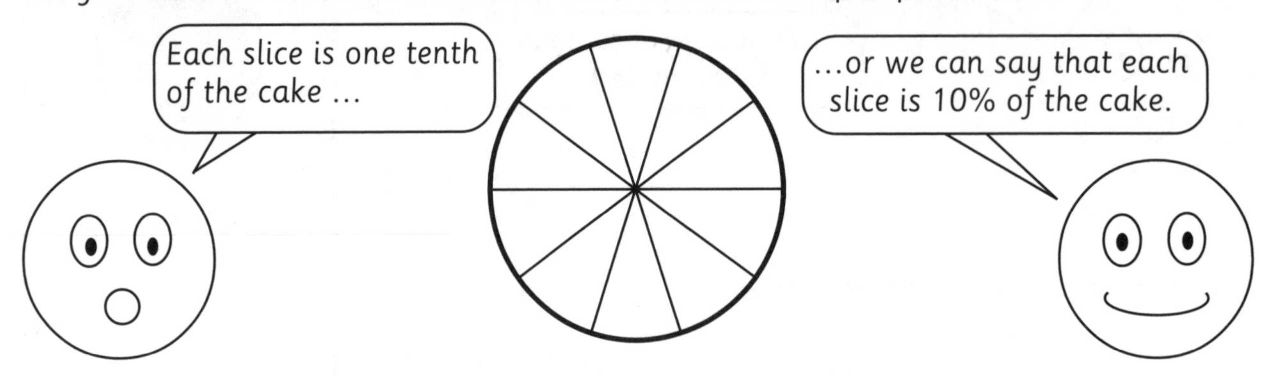

We can also say that each slice is 0·1 of the cake.

Look: $\frac{1}{10}$ = 10% = 0·1

Copy and complete the statements which are written under each picture below. The first one is done for you.

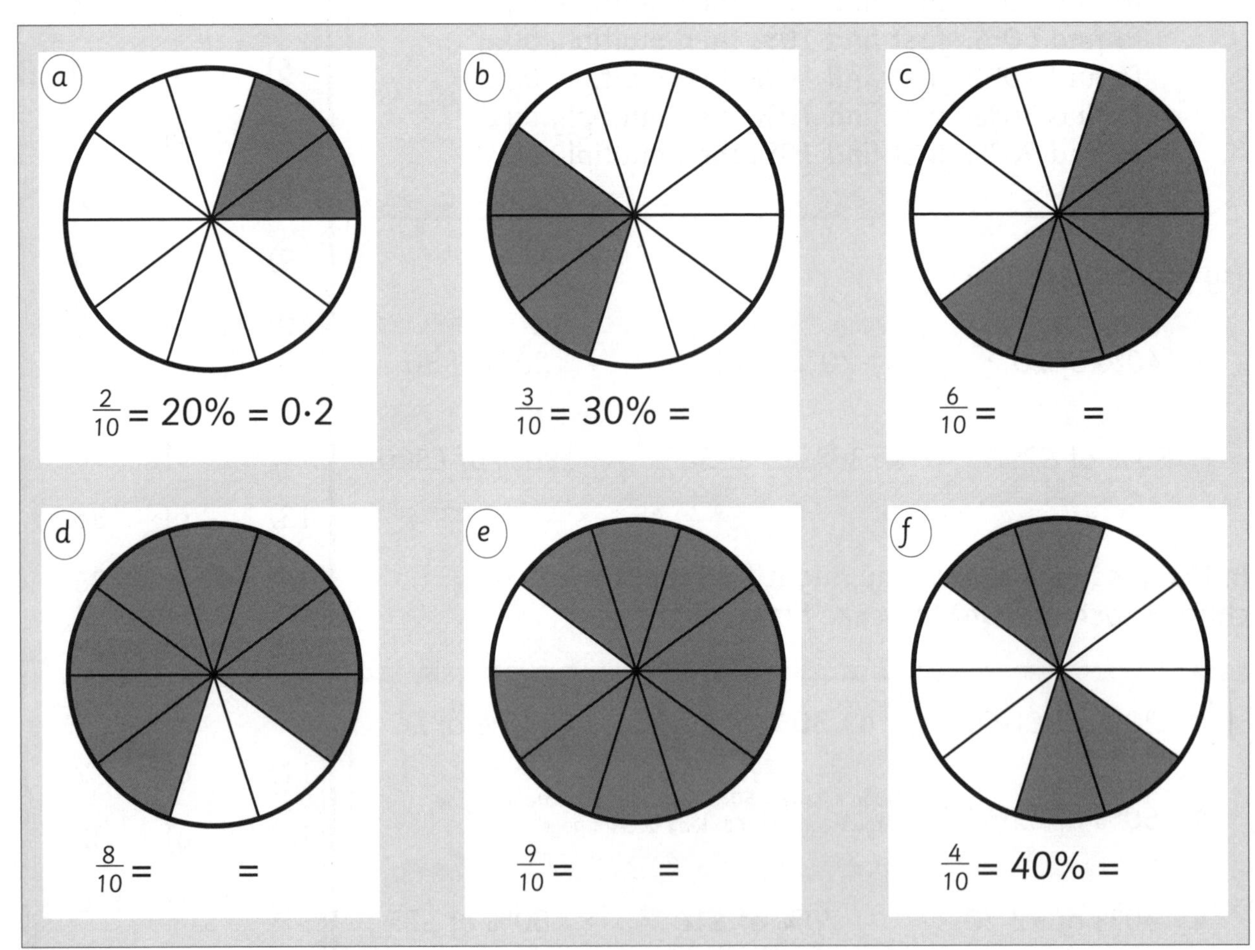

Here are some special facts which you need to know:

$\frac{1}{2}$ = 50% = 0·5

$\frac{1}{4}$ = 25% = 0·25

$\frac{3}{4}$ = 75% = 0·75

Coordinates

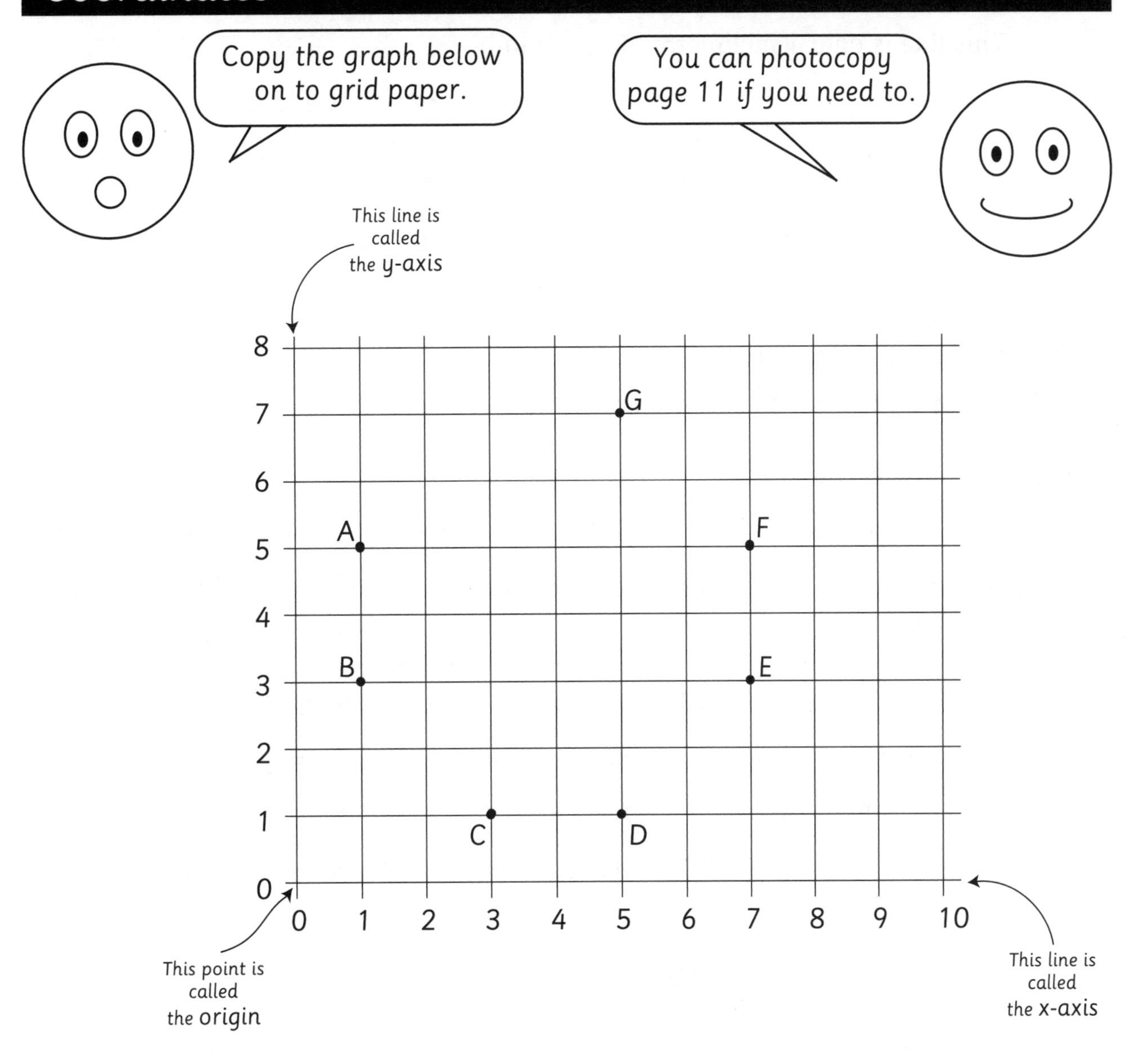

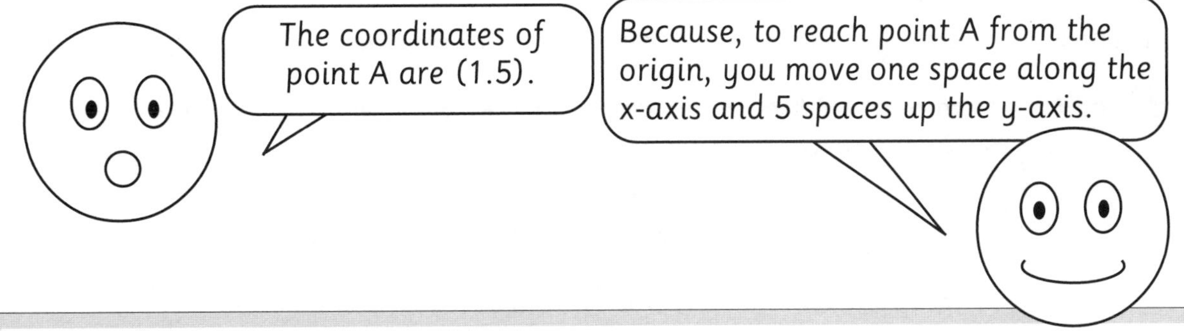

ⓐ Give the coordinates of points B, C, D, E, F and G.

ⓑ Draw lines joining A to B, B to C, C to D, D to E, E to F and F to G.

ⓒ You have drawn six sides of a symmetrical octagon. To complete the drawing, mark on the point where the final corner would be. Label this point 'H'. What are the coordinates of point H ?

ⓓ Now draw on the last two sides of the octagon.

Measurement of Length

This line is only 1 millimetre long. (1mm)

This line is 1 centimetre long. (1cm)

1 centimetre = 10 millimetres 1cm = 10mm

1mm = $\frac{1}{10}$cm 1mm = 0·1cm

How many millimetres are there in:

(a) 2 centimetres? (b) 6 centimetres? (c) $1\frac{1}{2}$ centimetres? (d) 3·5 centimetres?

Fill in the missing numbers:

(e) 7cm = mm (f) 5·2cm = mm (g) cm = 80mm (h) 2·6cm = mm

(i) cm = 45mm (j) cm =100mm (k) 12cm = mm (l) 1·7cm = mm

1 metre = 1000 millimetres 1m = 1000mm

1 mm = $\frac{1}{1000}$ m 10mm = $\frac{1}{100}$ m 100mm = $\frac{1}{10}$ m

1 mm = 0·001m 10mm = 0·01m 100mm = 0·1m

1 metre = 100centimetres 1m = 100cm

1cm = $\frac{1}{100}$m 10cm = $\frac{1}{10}$m

1cm = 0·01m 10cm = 0·1m

Fill in the missing numbers:

(m) 2m = cm (n) 4m = cm (o) m = 300cm (p) 2m = mm

(q) 3m = mm (r) 2·5m = cm (s) 6·1m = cm (t) 6·1m = mm

1 kilometre = 1000 metres 1km = 1000m

1 m = $\frac{1}{1000}$ km 10m = $\frac{1}{100}$ km 100m = $\frac{1}{10}$ km

1 m = 0·001km 10m = 0·01km 100m = 0·1km

Fill in the missing numbers:

(u) 3km = m (v) $3\frac{1}{2}$km = m (w) 2·5km = m (x) 1500m = km

(y) 4500m = km (z) 600m = km (A) 4·1km = m (B) 2900m = km

Measurement of Capacity

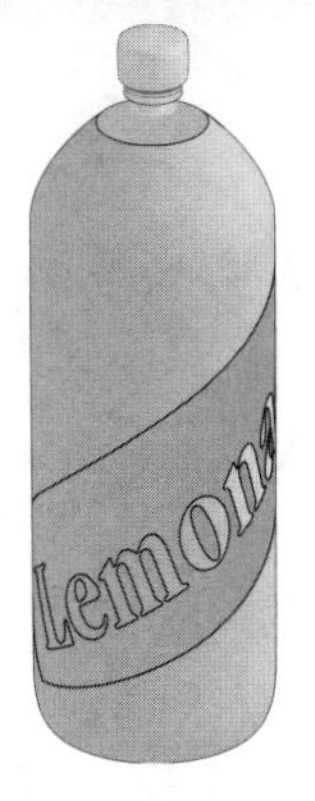

This bottle holds one litre of lemonade.

This spoon holds five millilitres.

This glass holds one hundred millilitres.

1 litre = 1000 millilitres   1l = 1000ml

1ml = $\frac{1}{1000}$l   10ml = $\frac{1}{100}$l   100ml = $\frac{1}{10}$l

1ml = 0·001l   10ml = 0·01l   100ml = 0·1l

(a) How many glasses could be filled from the bottle of lemonade?

(b) If only two glasses are filled, how much lemonade is left in the bottle?

(c) If we pour 0·5l of lemonade into glasses, how many glasses have we filled?

(d) If we filled a glass using the spoon shown above, how many spoonfuls would we need?

One and a half litres can be written in several ways:

$1\frac{1}{2}$l   1·5l   1l 500ml   1500ml

Write each of these amounts in two other ways:

(e) 1·2l   (f) 2·7l   (g) 3l 300ml   (h) 4600ml

Look at these examples:

5ml = 0·005l   42ml = 0·042l   317ml = 0·317l

Write each of these amounts in litres:

(i) 9ml   (j) 39ml   (k) 602ml   (l) 1674ml

Mental Speed

Time yourself to see how quickly you can answer these questions in your head.

1) Double 6
2) Double 11
3) Double 20
4) Double 16
5) Double 5
6) Double 13
7) Double 19
8) Double 8
9) Double 14
10) Double 12
11) Double 17
12) Double 9
13) Double 21
14) Double 23
15) Double 25
16) Double 50
17) Double 75
18) Double 80
19) Double 29
20) Double 61

Time taken:

[ ] seconds.

Division

Here are some division questions to answer.

If you get stuck, you could look back to Maths Today for ages 9-10.

(a) $6\overline{)42}$	(b) 54 ÷ 9	(c) 72 ÷ 8	(d) $4\overline{)48}$	(e) $6\overline{)51}$	(f) 35 ÷ 8
(g) $3\overline{)75}$	(h) $4\overline{)96}$	(i) $2\overline{)78}$	(j) $3\overline{)87}$	(k) $4\overline{)291}$	(l) 618 ÷ 3
(m) $5\overline{)742}$	(n) $2\overline{)909}$	(o) $6\overline{)348}$	(p) $7\overline{)432}$	(q) $8\overline{)900}$	(r) $6\overline{)400}$

Some of the questions above have a remainder.

But sometimes we don't want to have a remainder.

Look at this example: 29 ÷ 4  $\begin{array}{r} 7\text{ r}1 \\ 4\overline{)29} \end{array}$

Now see how we can find an answer without having a remainder.

First, we put in a decimal point then some noughts:	$4\overline{)29\cdot000}$
We start the division, but instead of having a remainder of one unit, we split the spare units into ten tenths.	$\begin{array}{r} 7\cdot \\ 4\overline{)29\cdot{}^{1}000} \end{array}$
Now we divide the ten tenths by 4, having two spares which we make into hundredths.	$\begin{array}{r} 7\cdot2 \\ 4\overline{)29\cdot{}^{1}0{}^{2}00} \end{array}$
Finally we divide the twenty hundredths by 4, giving an answer of five hundredths.	$\begin{array}{r} 7\cdot25 \\ 4\overline{)29\cdot{}^{1}0{}^{2}00} \end{array}$

Notice that we didn't use this nought but we had it there just in case.

Look carefully at another example, then try the questions below.

75 ÷ 8

Step 1: Write the question out carefully and prepare it for a decimal answer.

$$8\overline{)75{\cdot}0}$$

Note: If you need more noughts after the decimal point, you can put them in later.

Step 2: Start the division. Split the three spare units into thirty tenths.

$$\begin{array}{r} 9{\cdot} \\ 8\overline{)7 5{\cdot}{}^{3}0} \end{array}$$

Step 3: 30 ÷ 8 leaves six spare tenths. We will have to split these tenths into sixty hundredths:

$$\begin{array}{r} 9{\cdot}3 \\ 8\overline{)7 5{\cdot}{}^{3}0{}^{6}0} \end{array}$$

Step 4: 60 ÷ 8 leaves four spare hundredths. We will have to split these tenths into forty thousandths:

$$\begin{array}{r} 9{\cdot}37 \\ 8\overline{)7 5{\cdot}{}^{3}0{}^{6}0{}^{4}0} \end{array}$$

Step 5: Now we can find our final answer.

$$\begin{array}{r} 9{\cdot}375 \\ 8\overline{)7 5{\cdot}{}^{3}0{}^{6}0{}^{4}0} \end{array}$$

a) 41 ÷ 2	b) 38 ÷ 4	c) 51 ÷ 4	d) 67 ÷ 2
e) 73 ÷ 2	f) 49 ÷ 5	g) 91 ÷ 8	h) 141 ÷ 4
i) 100 ÷ 8	j) 117 ÷ 5	k) 125 ÷ 2	l) 250 ÷ 4

Mental Speed

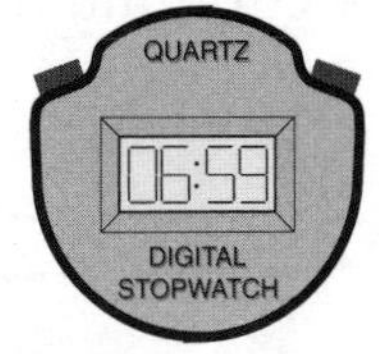

Time yourself to see how quickly you can answer these questions in your head.

1) + 6 = 30
2) 39 + = 50
3) 42 + = 100
4) + 63 = 100
5) + 75 = 100
6) 25 + = 200
7) + 75 = 400
8) 41 + = 300
9) + 13 = 500
10) + 113 = 500
11) + 251 = 500
12) 341 + = 600
13) 219 + = 700
14) + 187 = 800
15) + 250 = 750
16) 3·2 + = 4
17) 4·6 + = 5
18) 4·6 + = 10
19) 7·2 + = 10
20) + 2·1 = 10

Time taken:

☐ seconds.

More Decimal Divisions

Look carefully at this example:

39·2 ÷ 7 ⇨

$$\begin{array}{r} 5\cdot \\ 7\overline{)39\cdot{}^{4}2} \end{array}$$

5 x 7 = 35
so we have four spare units to make forty extra tenths... so we now have forty-two tenths.

$$\begin{array}{r} 5\cdot 6 \\ 7\overline{)39\cdot{}^{4}2} \end{array}$$

6 x 7 = 42
We have no spares so the question is finished.

Try these divisions:

(a) 23·5 ÷ 5	(b) 59·4 ÷ 6	(c) 33·2 ÷ 4	(d) 31·2 ÷ 8

Look at another example:

44·52 ÷ 6 ⇨

$$\begin{array}{r} 7\cdot \\ 6\overline{)44\cdot{}^{2}52} \end{array}$$

7 x 6 = 42
so we have two spare units to make twenty extra tenths... so we now have twenty-five tenths.

$$\begin{array}{r} 7\cdot 4 \\ 6\overline{)44\cdot{}^{2}5{}^{1}2} \end{array}$$

4 x 6 = 24
so we have one spare tenth to make ten extra hundredths... so we now have twelve hundredths.

$$\begin{array}{r} 7\cdot 42 \\ 6\overline{)44\cdot{}^{2}5{}^{1}2} \end{array}$$

2 x 6 = 12.
We have no spares so the question is finished.

Try these divisions:

(e) 25·28 ÷ 4	(f) 22·35 ÷ 3	(g) 68·46 ÷ 7	(h) 62·95 ÷ 5

Look at another example:

27·8 ÷ 4 ⇨

$$\begin{array}{r} 6\cdot \\ 4\overline{)27\cdot{}^{3}8} \end{array}$$

6 x 4 = 24
We make thirty extra tenths with the three spare units.

$$\begin{array}{r} 6\cdot 9 \\ 4\overline{)27\cdot{}^{3}8{}^{2}0} \end{array}$$

We put in an extra nought so that we can make twenty

$$\begin{array}{r} 6\cdot 95 \\ 4\overline{)27\cdot{}^{3}8{}^{2}0} \end{array}$$

Try these divisions:

(i) 23·7 ÷ 5	(j) 187·6 ÷ 8	(k) 38·1 ÷ 6	(l) 39·4 ÷ 8

Note: for question (l) you will need to put in more than one nought.

Square Numbers

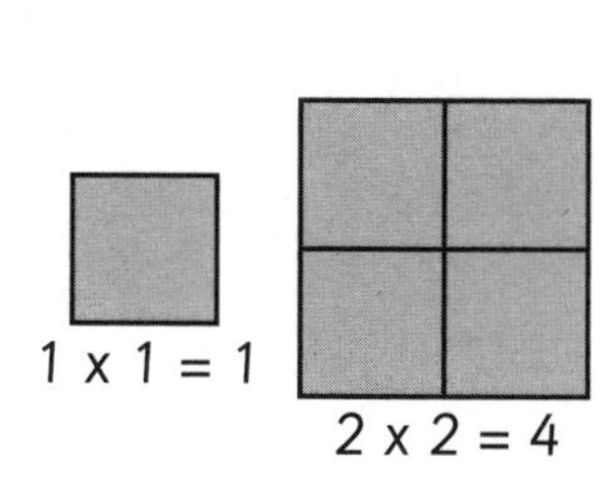
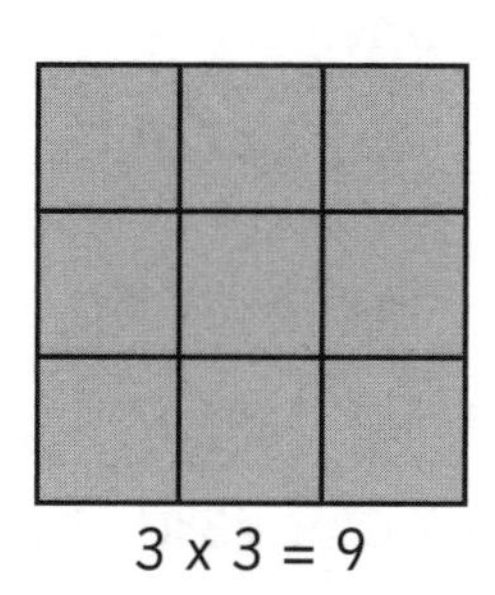
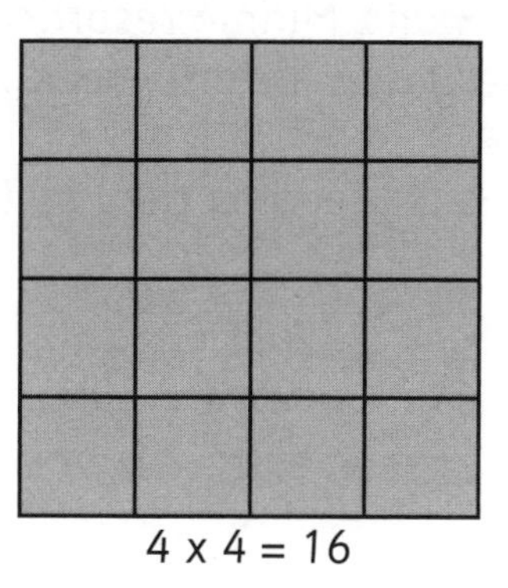

1 x 1 = 1 2 x 2 = 4 3 x 3 = 9 4 x 4 = 16

1, 4, 9 and 16 are called square numbers.
Instead of writing 3 x 3 = 9, we can write $3^2 = 9$
...we say 'three squared equals nine'.

Look: $1^2 = 1 \times 1 = 1$ one squared equals one
$2^2 = 2 \times 2 = 4$ two squared equals four
$4^2 = 4 \times 4 = 16$ four squared equals sixteen

Write the answers to these questions:

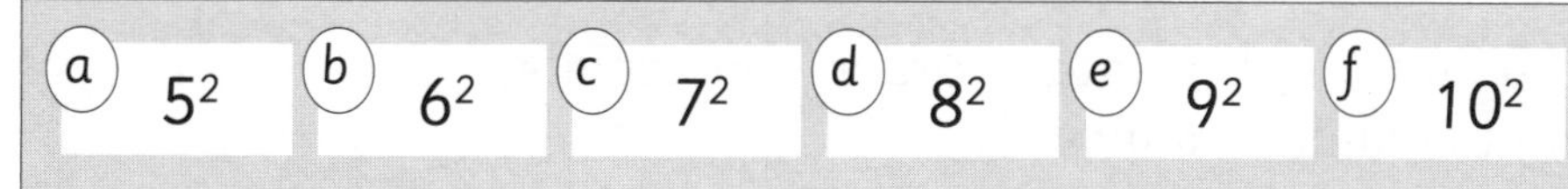

(a) 5^2 (b) 6^2 (c) 7^2 (d) 8^2 (e) 9^2 (f) 10^2

Look at this example:

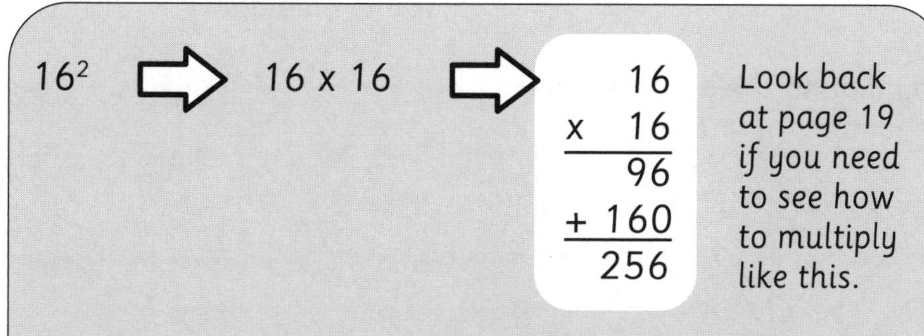

16^2 ⇨ 16 x 16 ⇨

```
   16
x  16
   96
+ 160
  256
```

Look back at page 19 if you need to see how to multiply like this.

...so sixteen squared equals two hundred and fifty-six.

Work out the answers to these questions:

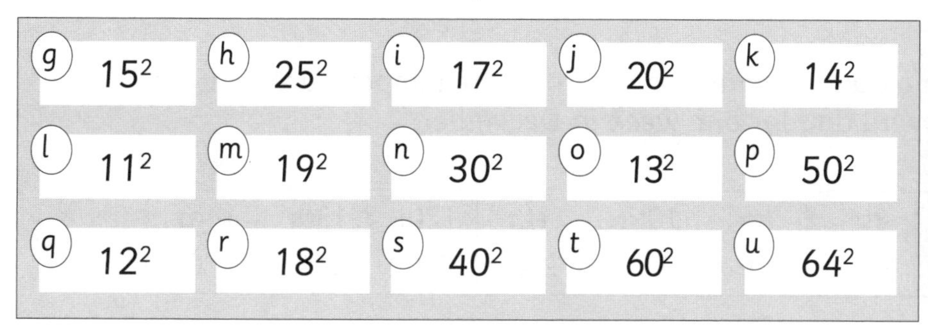

(g) 15^2 (h) 25^2 (i) 17^2 (j) 20^2 (k) 14^2

(l) 11^2 (m) 19^2 (n) 30^2 (o) 13^2 (p) 50^2

(q) 12^2 (r) 18^2 (s) 40^2 (t) 60^2 (u) 64^2

Mental Speed

Find the missing numbers as quickly as you can.

1) 100 – = 82
2) 100 – = 54
3) 100 – = 37
4) 100 – = 29
5) 100 – = 17
6) 100 – = 99
7) – 35 = 45
8) – 23 = 37
9) – 45 = 45
10) – 18 = 52
11) – 56 = 24
12) – 81 = 19
13) – 81 = 29
14) – 81 = 39
15) – 75 = 75
16) 200 – = 25
17) 300 – = 175
18) 400 – = 225
19) 500 – = 125
20) 800 – = 275

Time taken:

☐ seconds.

Handling Data

Max and Minnie recorded the temperature every day for one week in June.

This is the data they collected:

Date in June	8th	9th	10th	11th	12th	13th	14th
Temperature	21°C	22°C	23°C	23°C	23°C	22°C	20°C

We want to find the range, the mode, the median and the mean for this data.

Complete the answers below:

(a) The range is the highest value minus the lowest ...

... so the range = 23° – 20° = ☐

(b) The mode is the number which occurs most often in the list ...

... so we can see that the mode = ☐

(c) The median is found by putting the data in order from smallest to largest and finding the middle number ...

20° 21° 22° 22° 23° 23° 23°

... so the median = ☐

(d) The mean is found by adding the data together, then dividing by the number of entries ...

20° + 21° + 22° + 22° + 23° + 23° + 23° = 154°

There are seven entries ...

... so the mean = 154° ÷ 7 = ☐

Max and Minnie also recorded the temperature every day for one week in December:

Date in December	8th	9th	10th	11th	12th	13th	14th
Temperature	6°C	4°C	1°C	⁻2°C	0°C	0°C	5°C

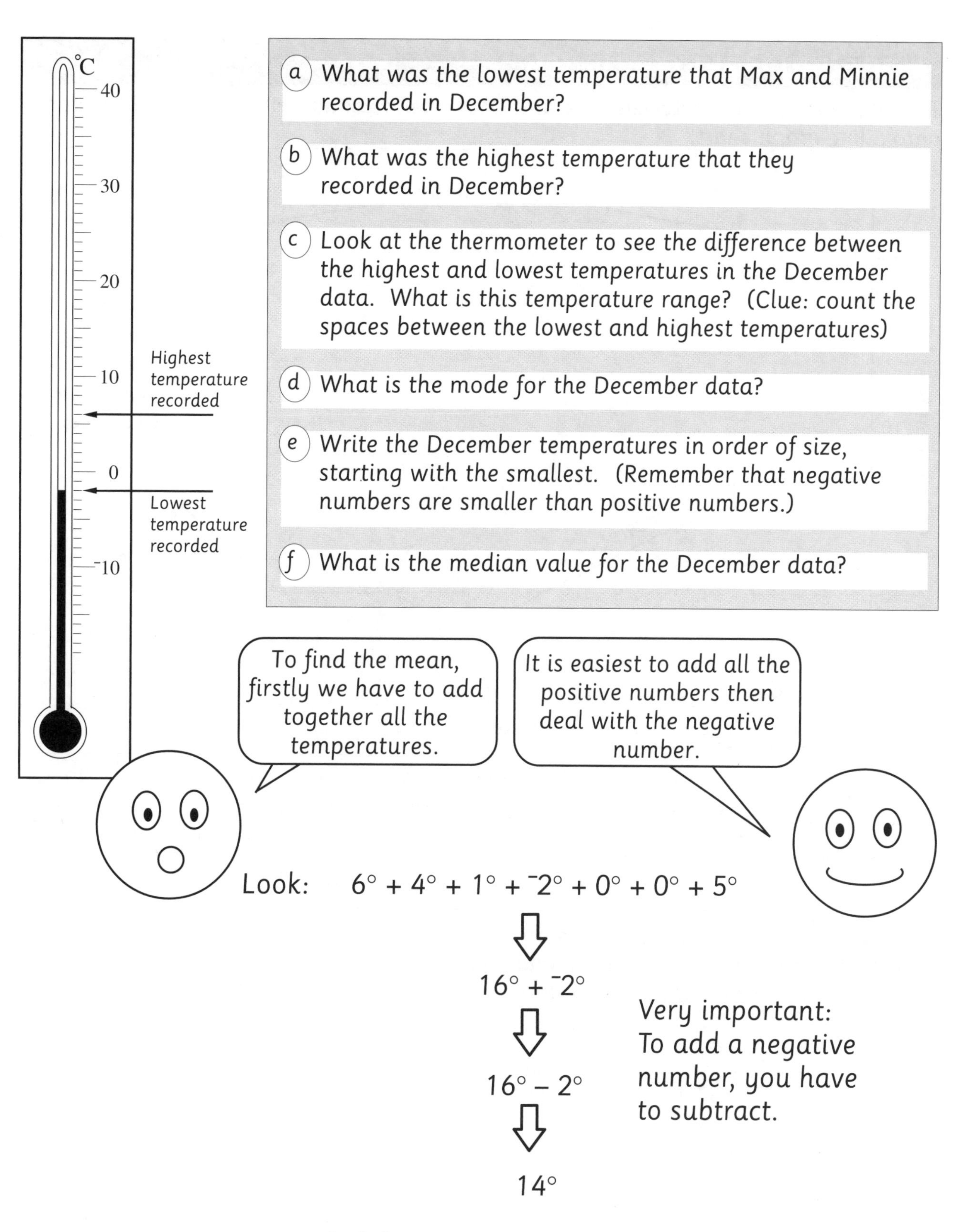

(a) What was the lowest temperature that Max and Minnie recorded in December?

(b) What was the highest temperature that they recorded in December?

(c) Look at the thermometer to see the difference between the highest and lowest temperatures in the December data. What is this temperature range? (Clue: count the spaces between the lowest and highest temperatures)

(d) What is the mode for the December data?

(e) Write the December temperatures in order of size, starting with the smallest. (Remember that negative numbers are smaller than positive numbers.)

(f) What is the median value for the December data?

Look: $6° + 4° + 1° + {}^{-}2° + 0° + 0° + 5°$

⇩

$16° + {}^{-}2°$

⇩

$16° - 2°$

⇩

$14°$

Very important:
To add a negative number, you have to subtract.

Now to find the mean temperature, we have to divide by seven (because seven temperatures were listed).

(g) What was the mean temperature for the week in December?

(h) How much more was the mean temperature in June than the mean temperature in December?

Handling Data continued

To make comparisons between June and December, Max and Minnie entered the data onto a line-graph chart:

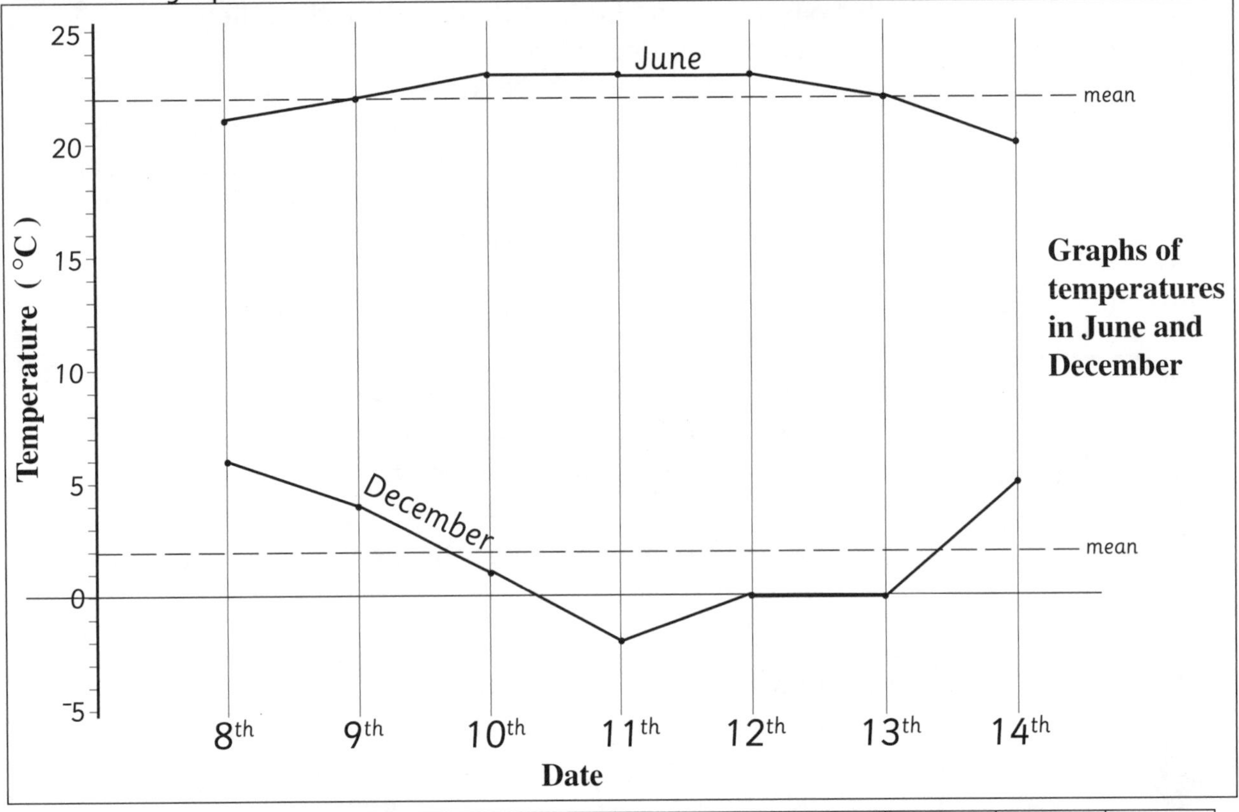

Here is some more temperature data.

Date in March	1st	2nd	3rd	4th	5th	6th	7th
Temperature	12°C	12°C	12°C	14°C	13°C	15°C	13°C
Date in September	1st	2nd	3rd	4th	5th	6th	7th
Temperature	18°C	17°C	17°C	18°C	20°C	18°C	18°C

(a) Copy the chart below and record on it the data for March and September. Don't forget to put a title and to label your chart. (b) What is the mean temperature for March? (c) What is the mean temperature for September?

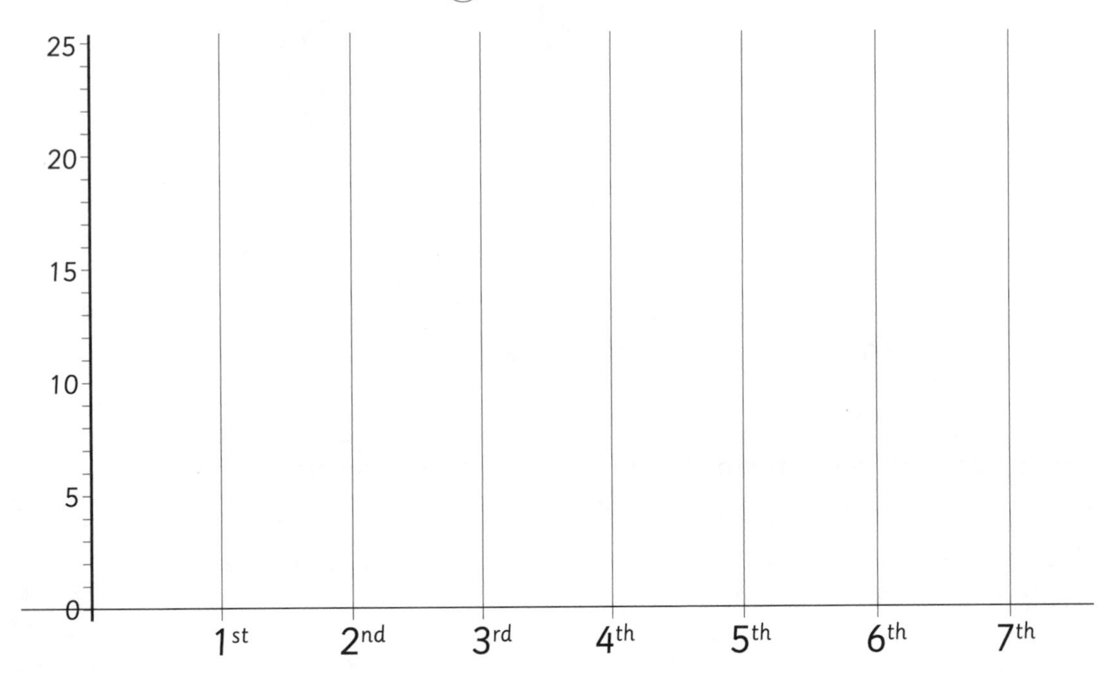

Max and Minnie drew pie-charts to show how they spend their time on a school day:

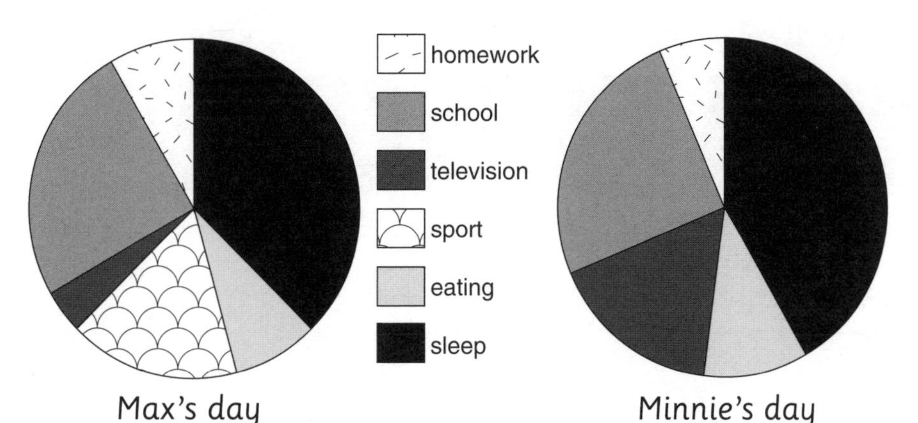

Don't forget ...

... that there are twenty-four hours in a day.

Answer these questions by looking at the pie-charts:

(a) Do Max and Minnie spend the same amount of time in school?

(b) How much time do they spend at school?

(c) Who sleeps the most?

(d) Who watches the television the most?

(e) Who does the most homework?

(f) Who does no sport?

(g) Estimate how much time Minnie spends watching television.

(h) Estimate how much time Max spends doing homework.

(i) Estimate the size of the angle made at the centre of the pie by the school segment of Max's chart.

(j) Estimate the size of the angle made at the centre of the pie by the sleep segment of Max's chart.

Mental Speed

Time yourself to see how quickly you can answer these questions in your head.

1) 6 x 7
2) 63 ÷ 9
3) 86 – 49
4) 92 + 108
5) 6^2
6) 3·2 + 2·4
7) 16 x 4
8) 72 ÷ 8
9) 28 ÷ 7
10) 8^2
11) 3·2 – 2·4
12) 23 x 10
13) 23 ÷ 10
14) 48 + 3·2
15) 7^2
16) $2^2 + 3^2$
17) $4^2 \div 2$
18) 2^2 – 1·2
19) 250 + 75
20) 250 – 75

Time taken:

☐ seconds.

Probability

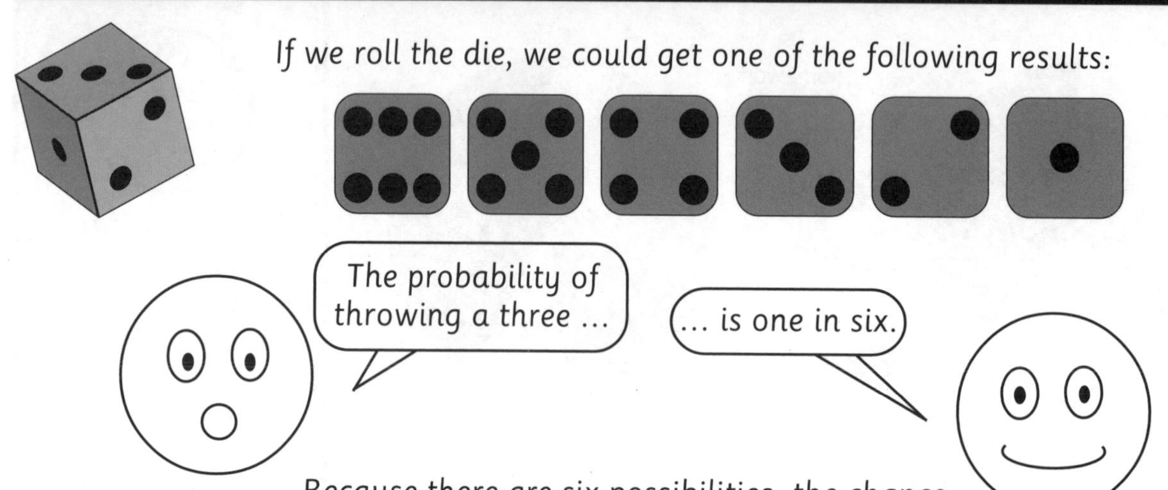

... Because there are six possibilities, the chance of getting a three is one possibility out of six.

We say that the **probability** is **one in six** or $\frac{1}{6}$

Answer these questions:

(a) What is the probability of throwing a two?

(b) What is the probability of throwing a five?

(c) What is the probability of throwing an even number?

Here are some letters from a game:

(d) If I put the letters in a bag, what is the probability of picking out a 'd' ?

(e) If I roll the die and pick a letter from the bag, which is more likely out of the following two possibilities: throwing a six or picking out a letter 'b' ?

Answer each of the questions below by using one of these words:

impossible unlikely likely certain

(f) The chance that I had a birthday last year is ...

(g) The chance that I visited Mars yesterday is ...

(h) The chance that I will visit the Moon in the next 20 years is ...

(i) The chance that I will travel in a car next year is ...